dedicated to
The Source Of All Being

NICHOLSON SOLAR ENERGY CATALOGUE

Nick Nicholson

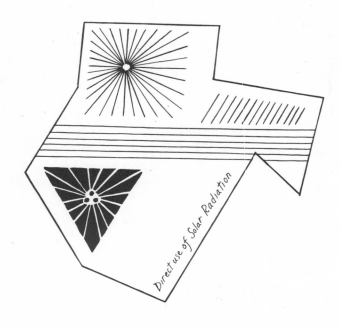

Direct use of Solar Radiation

NICHOLSON SOLAR ENERGY CATALOGUE

Plain talk from NICK NICHOLSON

Dear Subscriber,

You have in your hands the First Edition of the Nicholson
Solar Energy Catalogue. I believe a word or two is in
order concerning its purpose.

The catalogue is being offered in response to the present
need for information pertaining to the practical application
of solar energy and related systems. It has a dual nature.
One aspect is commercial, the other is a non-commercial,
unbiased effort to disseminate useful information.

My credentials for taking part in what is popularly being called "the energy revolution"
are as follows:

As Of February, 1977...

1. Participation in the design and successful completion of seven solar homes.

2. Design and construction of the National Research Council Solar Demonstration House
   at Ayer's Cliff in conjunction with Direct Energy Associates.

3. Design, construction and funding of Solar I, which has been available to the public,
   news media and educational institutions for the past three years.

4. Last but not least, participation in the drudgery attached to pioneer efforts in any
   field. Separating the wheat from the chaff and reducing propositions to their simplest
   practical form. Theories and pure research have their valued place in the scheme of
   things but, in the final analysis, it is the guy in the back room that gets the proposition
   to work. Meeting and exchanging information with these "back roomers" has been an
   arduous though gratifying experience. It is upon this continuous exchange that I place
   my faith that this catalogue will fulfill its purpose.

I would like to extend an open invitation to interested parties to submit constructive
criticism of this catalogue with a view towards making it better to fulfill its function.

Nick Nicholson

219992

NICHOLSON SOLAR ENERGY CATALOGUE

WHAT DO YOU RECEIVE WHEN YOU BUY THIS CATALOGUE?

1.   The catalogue as you see it.

     PLUS

2.   All the updates containing information that becomes available after the catalogue went to print. The updates will be mailed to you automatically and free of charge by filling out the coupon on the last page and mailing it to: THE NICHOLSON SOLAR ENERGY CATALOGUE

      P.O. BOX 125   P.O. Box 216
      AYER'S CLIFF, QUEBEC J0B 1C0   FRENCHTOWN, NEW JERSEY 08825

     Requests for updates must be accompanied by the coupon.

Note: To receive your updates for this catalogue, do not complete the coupon below.
      Only use the coupon on the inside last page.

The Nicholson Solar Energy Catalogue
P.O. Box 125
Ayer's Cliff, Quebec J0B 1C0

Gentlemen:

I have recently purchased a copy of your 1977 catalogue and I would like to receive by return mail, at no extra cost, all updates for the year 1977.

Please send updates to: (please print clearly)

Name

Street Address

City or Town

Province or State   Postal Code

Country

I obtained my catalogue from

SPECIMEN

NICHOLSON SOLAR ENERGY CATALOGUE

SECTION 1

OUTLINES FOR SOLAR HOMES

SOLAR I

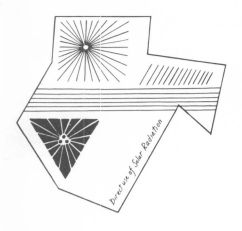

Direct use of Solar Radiation

SPECIFICATIONS

Dimensions . . . . 16' x 24' x 12'
Interior Space . . . . 448 square feet
Solar System . . . . Air/Rock
Collector Area . . . . 192 square feet
Storage Volume . . . . 192 cubic feet
Back-Up System . . . . Wood/Electric

1—2

EAST

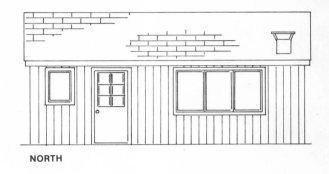

NORTH

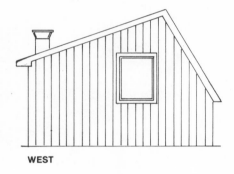

WEST

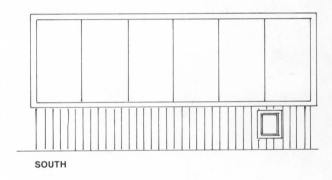

SOUTH

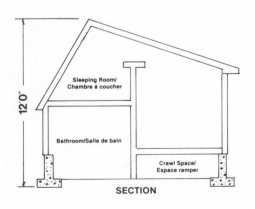

Sleeping Room/
Chambre à coucher

Bathroom/Salle de bain

Crawl Space/
Espace ramper

12'0"

SECTION

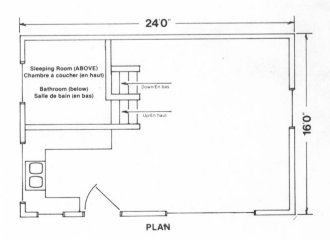

24'0"

Sleeping Room (ABOVE)
Chambre à coucher (en haut)

Bathroom (below)
Salle de bain (en bas)

Down/En bas

Up/En haut

16'0"

PLAN

NICHOLSON SOLAR ENERGY CATALOGUE

SOLAR II

SPECIFICATIONS

Dimensions . . . . 30' x 26' x 17'
Interior Space . . . . 900 square feet
Solar System . . . . Air/Rock
Collector Area . . . . 250 square feet
Storage Volume . . . . 500 cubic feet
Back-Up System . . . . Wood/Electric

NICHOLSON SOLAR ENERGY CATALOGUE

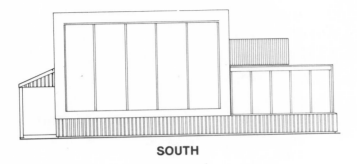

SOUTH

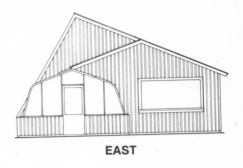

EAST

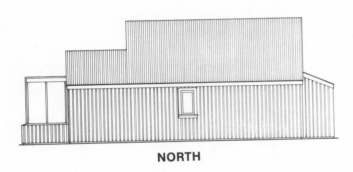

NORTH

WEST

GROUND LEVEL

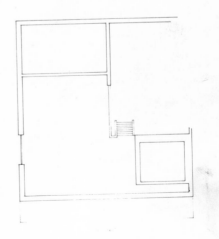

FIRST LEVEL

1—5

NICHOLSON SOLAR ENERGY CATALOGUE

SOLAR III

SPECIFICATIONS

Dimensions	24' x 24' x 24'
Interior space	1320 square feet
Solar System	Air/Rock
Collector Area	400 square feet
Storage Volume	600 Cubic Feet
Back-Up System	Wood/Electric

NICHOLSON SOLAR ENERGY CATALOGUE

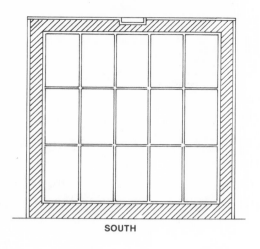

SOUTH

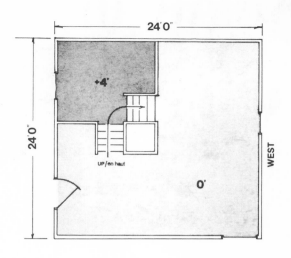

24'0"

24'0"

+4'

UP/en haut

WEST

0'

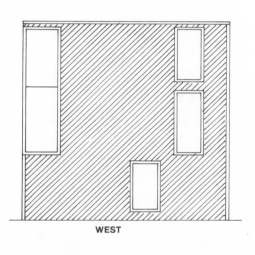

WEST

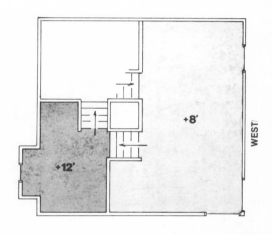

+8'

+12'

WEST

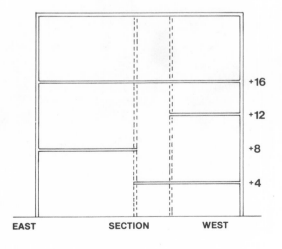

EAST   SECTION   WEST

+16

+12

+8

+4

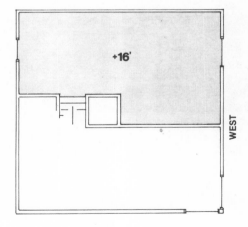

+16'

WEST

NICHOLSON SOLAR ENERGY CATALOGUE

SOLAR IV

SPECIFICATIONS

Dimensions . . . . 16' x 28' x 18'
plus 10' x 28' Porch
Interior Space . . . . 576 square feet
Solar System . . . . Air/Rock
Collector Area . . . . 300 square feet
Storage Volume . . . . 1200 cubic feet
Back-Up System . . . . Wood/Electric

PROJECT UNDER CONSTRUCTION
FINISHED PHOTOGRAPH NOT AVAILABLE

NICHOLSON SOLAR ENERGY CATALOGUE

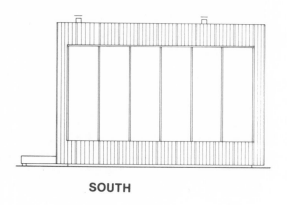

SOUTH

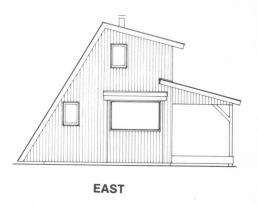

EAST

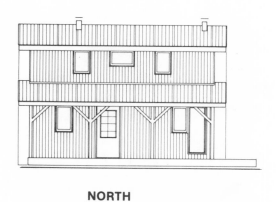

NORTH

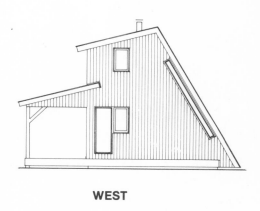

WEST

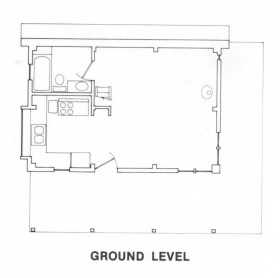

GROUND LEVEL

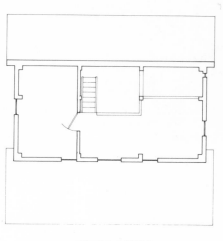

FIRST LEVEL

NICHOLSON SOLAR ENERGY CATALOGUE

SOLAR V

SPECIFICATIONS

Dimensions . . . . 30' x 28' x 17'
Interior Space . . . . 960 square feet
Solar System . . . . Air/Rock
Collector Area . . . . 350 square feet
Storage Volume . . . . 700 cubic feet
Back-Up System . . . . Wood/Electric

NICHOLSON SOLAR ENERGY CATALOGUE

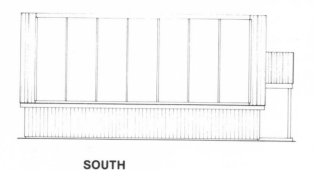

SOUTH

EAST

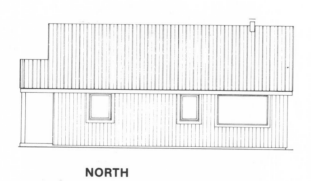

NORTH

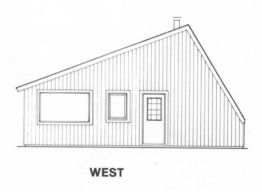

WEST

GROUND LEVEL

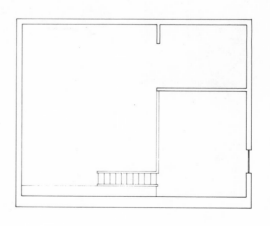

FIRST LEVEL

1—11

NICHOLSON SOLAR ENERGY CATALOGUE

SOLAR VI

SPECIFICATIONS

Dimensions . . . . 22' x 28' x 22'
Interior Space . . . . 1100 square feet
Solar System . . . . Air/Rock
Collector Area . . . . 400 square feet
Storage Volume . . . . 800 cubic feet
Back-Up System . . . . Wood/Electric

PROJECT UNDER CONSTRUCTION
FINISHED PHOTOGRAPH NOT AVAILABLE
SEE UPDATES

NICHOLSON SOLAR ENERGY CATALOGUE

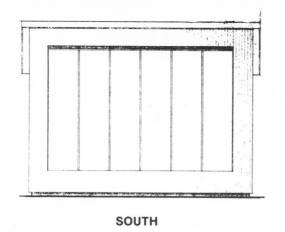

SOUTH

EAST

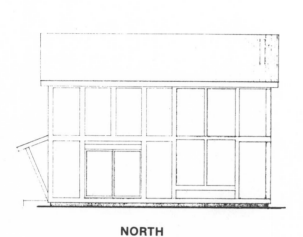

NORTH

WEST

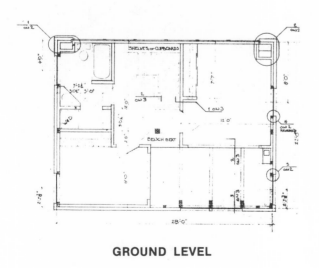

GROUND LEVEL

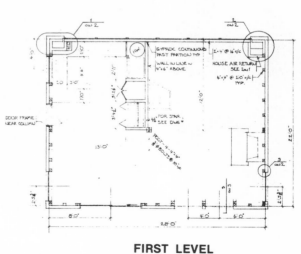

FIRST LEVEL

1—13

NICHOLSON SOLAR ENERGY CATALOGUE

SOLAR VII

SPECIFICATIONS

Dimensions . . . . 16' x 20' x 22'
Interior Space . . . . 320 square feet
Solar System . . . . Air/Rock (passive)
Collector Area . . . . 104 square feet
Storage Volume . . . . 160 cubic feet
Back-Up System . . . . Wood

NICHOLSON SOLAR ENERGY CATALOGUE

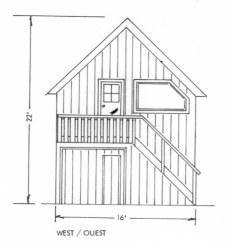

WEST / OUEST

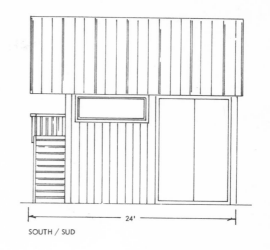

SOUTH / SUD

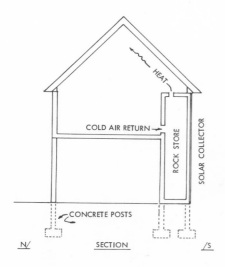

HEAT

COLD AIR RETURN

ROCK STORE

SOLAR COLLECTOR

CONCRETE POSTS

N/   SECTION   /S

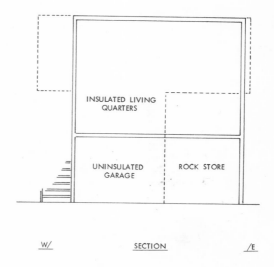

INSULATED LIVING QUARTERS

UNINSULATED GARAGE

ROCK STORE

W/   SECTION   /E

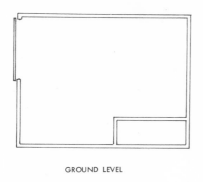

GROUND LEVEL

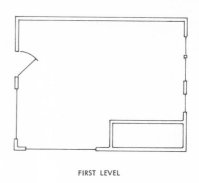

FIRST LEVEL

1—15

NICHOLSON SOLAR ENERGY CATALOGUE

SOLAR VIII
(PROJECT)

SPECIFICATIONS

Dimensions	26' x 32' x 25'
Interior Space	1415 square feet
Solar System	Air/Rock
Collector Area	384 square feet
Storage Volume	1000 cubic feet
Back-Up System	Wood/Electric

By JOHN HODKINSON, Arch.

Solar VIII is a medium sized, three bedroom house designed for energy efficient, comfortable living in the country.

Upstairs, the large master bedroom has a view to the west, while the two smaller bedrooms face east. The fully equipped main bathroom and the laundry area are on the north and south walls, respectively. There is space for a sewing area next to the laundry area, under the skylight at the head of the stairs.

Downstairs, the entrance from the car area is through a heated vestibule with a large coat closet. The room adjoining serves as a private study or work area. The fully equipped kitchen has a pass through counter to the dining area. The dining room has a view to the south through large, double casement windows.

The library, living area and greenhouse spaces occupies the west end of the house with a large picture-bay window. The living area is centered around a 36" rustic fireplace which incorporates a warm air heating device to supply warmed fresh air to the house.

The floors are varnished pine. The ceilings have functional 7 inch by 7 inch wood beams. The outside is finished in vertical pine boards, stained with a creosote stain and left to weather to a barnwood grey.

The solar heating system, except for the roof top collector, is located in the basement. It is fully automatic, incorporating a variable speed fan for solar heating and an electric furnace to move the air for house heating. The electric resistance heater in the furnace cuts in automatically only when there is no solar heat available.

SOUTH

EAST

NORTH

WEST

GROUND LEVEL

FIRST LEVEL

1—17

NICHOLSON SOLAR ENERGY CATALOGUE

STANDARD PLANS

Standard plans for houses Solar VI and Solar VIII are now available.

They include all details for the solar heating system and the house construction.

The plans include:

Architectural layouts

Construction details

Electrical plan

Plumbing plan

List of materials

All details for the solar heating system
and the back-up electrical system

Requests for information and orders for
house plans should be directed to:

JOHN HODKINSON, Arch.
10 BURTON AVENUE
WESTMOUNT, QUEBEC H3Z 1J7

NICHOLSON SOLAR ENERGY CATALOGUE

SEQUENTIAL SERIES

This special supplement to the sections of the Nicholson Solar Energy Catalogue will feature continuous sequential photographs of the more interesting solar home installations.

The purpose in so doing is to provide visual help for the do-it-yourselfer as well as the professional entering the era of new age building techniques. That the forgoing may be a bit presumptious, I am painfully aware. However, there are drastic demands being made today via the energy/inflation crisis and there must be new systems to meet these demands.

The following sequential photographs are of Solar VI. They begin with the foundation and proceed to the point when the deadline for this manuscript was reached. This illustrates the reason for the update service. There is always something more to come. All important details for the remainder of the project will be forthcoming with the update service.

I hope that you find this approach interesting and helpful.

Sincerly,

Nick Nicholson

NICHOLSON SOLAR ENERGY CATALOGUE

1. Footing forms with steel rebars in place.

2. Completed footing with perimeter drain in place.

4. Concrete blocks in place.

1—20

3. The crushed stone in the picture is placed over
a continuous polyethylene vapor barrier.

5. View inside the rock store.

1—21

NICHOLSON SOLAR ENERGY CATALOGUE

6. Polyethylene vapor barrier in place. Do not forget to leave
a small opening in the bottom in case of rain during construction.

9. Cement block plenums. Note spaces between blocks for air infiltration.
Note inlet opening in side of store.

NICHOLSON SOLAR ENERGY CATALOGUE

7. First layer of styrene in place.

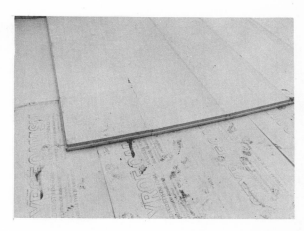

8. Close up of second styrene layer. Note shiplap edges and staggered joints.

10. Fill 'er up!

11. Close up of store partially filled with crushed stone and inlet opening covered with waterproof plywood.

NICHOLSON SOLAR ENERGY CATALOGUE

12. Crushed stone in place.

13. Placing the first layer of insulation.

15. Sealing and taping aspenite joints.

16. Close up of tape applied over non hardening butyl rubber base sealant.

NICHOLSON SOLAR ENERGY CATALOGUE

14. First layer of insulation in place and first sheet of aspenite in place.

17. 2" x 8" floor joists in place with second layer of insulation being fitted.

1—25

18. Finishing off the rock store with plywood sub flooring.

19. Detail of the exhaust side port of the rock store.

21. South and west walls, ground level in place.

NICHOLSON SOLAR ENERGY CATALOGUE

20. Ground level of south wall framed and ready for aspenite cover.

22. Ground level of east wall and center beam in place.

1—27

23. First floor completed and framing begins for second level of the south wall.

25. Close up of exposed pine rafters and temporary bracing on west wall.

24. South wall in place. The wind was blowing so we left the upper layer of aspenite for later.

26. Days end.

1—29

27. 11:00 A.M. On the roof. Foil backed gypsum board being placed...carefully.

29. 2:30 P.M. 2" x 8" overlays in place perpendicular to rafters below gypsum board.

1—30

28. 12:45 P.M. Aluminum foil tape over the joints.

30. 3:00 P.M. Insulation in place and ready for aluminum roofing.

1—31

31. 6:00 P.M. Aluminum roofing in place.

By employing the technique of working up instead of down, the roofing sequence shown here took exactly 6 1/2 hours to complete.

Gravity is your friend, let it work for you, not against you.

Other advantages of this system include:

1. <u>Minimum taping of gypsum board joints</u>. Normally, a ceiling of this size will require the taping, filling and sanding of 160 feet of joints. All to be done while working over your head. This system requires the finishing of only 28 feet of joints. The rest of the joints are hidden above the exposed rafters.

2. <u>Aesthetic appeal</u>. The exposing of the rafters to the interior view adds to the design of the home.

3. <u>Air tightness</u>. Taping the joints in this manner produces continuous vapor and air tightness.

4. <u>Speed and economy</u>. Experience has shown a marked increase in these factors.

1—32

32. Aspenite layer on south wall completed. (See collector fabrication sequence for details.)

33. First layer of foil backed gypsum board applied to east wall.

NICHOLSON SOLAR ENERGY CATALOGUE

34. Foil backed gypsum board taped to styrene surrounding the foundation.

35. Taping joints over doors and windows.

36. Applying 2" x 4" firring.

Continued in updates . . .

SECTION 2

DESIGN CONSIDERATIONS

— NOTES —

INTRODUCTION

Incorporating a solar system into a house design involves several factors that are not ordinarily encountered in conventional home design. Some of these design considerations are:

* Elimination of some, if not all, of the windows on the south facing wall.

* Orientation of the house to obtain the maximum exposure of the south wall to the sun.

* Innovative interior designs to maximize use of the east, west and north walls for light penetration, ventilation and aesthetic purposes.

* Upgrading insulation techniques to minimize heat losses. Infiltration losses (air leaks) account for up to 30% of the heat loss from the average house.

And...with todays trend towards smaller, less costly, energy efficient homes, some practical tips on personalizing your interior spaces through the use of open planning, exposed frames and natural materials.

Typical interiors of Solar I and Solar II

2—1

NICHOLSON SOLAR ENERGY CATALOGUE

Optimizing the use of money, time and materials for the building of a home requires an efficient design to work from.

An efficient design is the result of intelligent planning.

Intelligent planning requires thought.

What is there to think about? Let's look at some of the current building practices and see what we can learn.

Here is a scene that is familiar to everyone. We have a typical farmhouse with the wood placed horizontally and painted white. The owner has been painting the house every three years, effectively sealing in moisture as well as screening out the rain. The result is that after 40 years of continuous maintenance, the wood is beginning to rot out.

Now look at the barn. The wood has been standing there an equal length of time. It has been given no maintenance. There is usually no rot and the wood is still good for another 40 years and then some.

Why? Simply because the wood was placed vertical instead of horizontal. Wood will not rot if it is completely wet or completely dry. It is when it is kept damp that it begins to rot. Like a straw, wood placed vertically drains well and tends to stay dry.

Windows have three primary functions: light, ventilation and views. Picture windows which tend to be expensive, are justified on the basis of the panoramic view that they afford. Why they are placed facing the street instead of a four season landscaped rear yard is something that I have never quite understood.

View from the road

View from the back yard

An early (pre-solar) Nicholson house built from recycled materials

2—2

Many houses have too many opening windows. Less opening windows, strategically placed, can be more effective for summer ventilation. An open window high on the south or west side and one or two open windows low on the north or east side will help create a thermosyphon action that moves cool air through the house.

A feature of fixed glazing (non opening) windows is that a small window (lower cost) placed higher on a wall will have the effect of admitting more light than a large window (higher cost) placed low on a wall. This is due to the light from the higher window penetrating the interior of the room more effectively.

Another example of increasing natural light through window placement is to put a tall, thin window Adjacent to a white wall. The entering light sweeps the wall and reflects into the room.

Interiors on this page are of the first house built by Nicholson from information obtained from the Whole Earth Catalogue.

2—3

NICHOLSON SOLAR ENERGY CATALOGUE

DESIGN CONSIDERATION NO - NO's

If you must, add some protection
to help out

* Entries under eaves

* Dark hallways

* Hallways

* High maintenance materials

* Unnecessary partitions

* Sterile bathrooms

* Poor insulation

* Long staircases

* Air leaks

* Going over your budget

* 150 watt light bulbs
  (Several smaller bulbs give better glare
    free light and save money in the long run)

NICHOLSON SOLAR ENERGY CATALOGUE

Fireplace in the wall keeps things cozy during dreary winter days.

Large mirror creates illusion of roominess in this 8' x 12' bathroom.

2—4.1

NICHOLSON SOLAR ENERGY CATALOGUE

Roomy shower from recycled bricks.

Practical use of a picture window.

NICHOLSON SOLAR ENERGY CATALOGUE

SITE ORIENTATION

The south facing wall may be oriented between <u>true</u> south (not magnetic south) to 10° west of true south.

True south can be determined by using a compass to determine magnetic south and correcting for deviation. Deviation (the difference between magnetic and true compass directions) varies with each geographic location. Information on deviation is readily available from any nearby airport.

Another way of determining true south is to place a stick vertically in the ground at 12 o'clock noon, standard time, and mark the shadow.

A third method, for those who know their astronomy, is to place two sticks in line with the north star.

2—5

NICHOLSON SOLAR ENERGY CATALOGUE

SINGLE vs. DOUBLE GLAZING

Opinion is split concerning the actual impact on efficiency of double glazing vs. single glazing.

single glazed   double glazed

This picture shows clearly that the double glazed unit on this front pass collector module is reflecting more sun light than the single glazed module.

The greater penetration of sunlight entering the single glazed unit produces greater heat gain

The advocates of double glazing maintain that the heat loss due to reflection is offset by the insulating quality of the double glazed unit.

Typical detail of monitor utilized on test modules

Daily observations at Ayer's Cliff have shown that approximately 90% of annual collector operation occurs when the ambiant temperature is above 20° F.

Results from tests conducted at Ayer's Cliff indicate clearly that in the ambiant temperature range of 20° F to 60° F, the single glazed unit collected heat 2° to 7° higher than the double glazed unit.

On the few occasions when the ambiant air temperature went below 20° F, usually late in the day at the very end of the solar period, the trend reversed itself in favor of the double glazed unit.

From personal observations, the works of others and by extension, I advocate that subject to further developements, single glazing be given preference for all back pass collectors and excepting solar installations in extremely cold regions, for all front pass systems as well.

2—6

Sloped Collectors	vs.	Vertical Collectors

Advantages

* Maximum solar penetration per square foot

* Captures more of the diffuse radiation from overcast skies

Advantages

* Captures reflected light from snow

* Relatively easy to build

* No tendency toward snow and ice build-up

* Simplifies interior planning

Disadvantages

* Misses reflected light from snow

* Relatively difficult to build

* Tendency towards snow and ice build-up

* Needs summer cooling in all climates

* Complicates interior planning

Disadvantages

* Approximately 6% loss of solar penetration per square foot

* Misses most of the diffuse radiation from overcast skies

CALCULATING SOLAR SYSTEM EFFICIENCY

The basic format for the following calculations courtesy of the KALWALL CORPORATION

This section is designed to give some idea of how to calculate heating needs with a view towards estimating the percentage of heat that should be supplied by a given solar system for a particular house design.

The format is organized to minimize the steps required to arrive at a conclusion. It is not intended to be an engineering study.

The two major factors that determine heating requirements are: (1) the local climate and (2) the heat loss or insulation value of the house. The following is one of several methods of estimating heat loss. As a convenient example to demonstrate the method, we will use a small house located in Ayer's Cliff, Quebec.

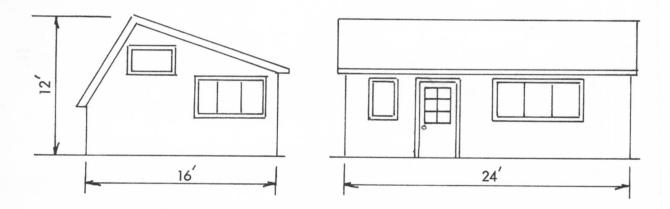

A METHOD TO CALCULATE HEAT LOSS (refer to sample calculation sheet)

Part 1 ......Temperature Factor

The first step in determining heat loss is finding the temperature factor. First, write down in the appropriate space on the sample calculation sheet the temperature at which you wish to keep your house. We used 70° F for our Ayer's Cliff house. Next, look up your city (or a city with a similar climate) in table I. For Ayer's Cliff, the value is –11 (the closest city with the same climate is Rock Island). Now, subtract the design temperature value obtained from table I from the house temperature and you will have the "temperature factor". For our Ayer's Cliff house it is 70 – (–11) = 81. For convenience, we will use 80 as the temperature factor.

Part 2 ......Infiltration Factor

The second step in determining heat loss requires measuring your house. First, find the dimensions (in feet) of all exterior surfaces, including walls, windows, doors, ceiling, etc. Write these dimensions in the appropriate spaces on the sample calculation sheet.

NICHOLSON SOLAR ENERGY CATALOGUE

The Ayer's Cliff house is a single story, 16 X 24 feet, with 1 door and 6 windows.

From the dimensions, calculate the area and perimeter of each door and window and write them down in the appropriate spaces. For the Ayer's Cliff house, we calculated as follows:

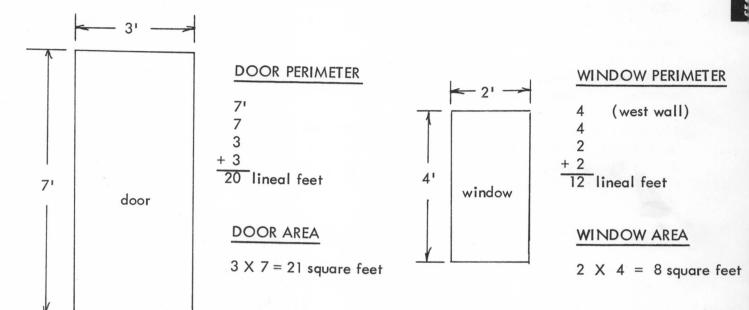

DOOR PERIMETER

```
  7'
  7
  3
+ 3
 20  lineal feet
```

DOOR AREA

3 X 7 = 21 square feet

WINDOW PERIMETER

```
  4   (west wall)
  4
  2
+ 2
 12  lineal feet
```

WINDOW AREA

2 X 4 = 8 square feet

Now, look up in table II the type of window or door and find the value listed under the temperature factor for your house. This value is the infiltration factor and should be written down in the appropriate space on the sample calculation sheet. For our Ayer's Cliff house, with casement windows, and under the temperature factor of 80°, a value of 75° is found and written down for infiltration factor on our calculation sheet.

Finally, multiply each window and door primeter by its infiltration loss factor to obtain its infiltration loss and then add up the infiltration losses to get a total infiltration loss.

Part 3 ......Conduction Losses

The third step in determining heat loss is calculating the conduction losses. From the dimensions found in Part 2, calculate the gross area of each surface and write it down in the appropriate space. For our Ayer's Cliff house, the south wall is 4' high by 24' wide and has a gross area of 96 square feet. Also, calculate the areas of the windows and doors and write them down in the appropriate spaces. In order that the windows and doors not be counted twice for conduction losses, this area must be subtracted from the gross wall area (96 square feet in our example) to get a net area of 90 square feet. The net area for the other walls is calculated in similar fashion.

NICHOLSON SOLAR ENERGY CATALOGUE

Next, look up in Table III the type of wall, ceiling, floor, door or window construction and find the value listed under the temperature factor for your house. This value is the heat loss factor and should be written down in the appropriate space on the sample calculation sheet for your house. For our Ayer's Cliff house, the south wall, which is above grade with wood siding and 3 1/2" insulation, the value under a temperature factor of 80° is "7". This is written down as the heat loss factor. Different construction techniques have different factors and each must be found.

Next, multiply each net area by its heat loss factor to get the heat loss through each surface. Add these numbers up to get the total heat loss by conduction.

Finally, add the infiltration loss to the conduction loss to get the approximate maximum heating requirement in BTU's/hour for your house. For the Ayer's Cliff house, this is 21,971 BTU's/hour.

Part 4 ......Average Heating Requirements – Degree Days

In Part 3 we calculated the maximum heating requirement in BTU's/hour. This is the number most often used for sizing conventional furnaces. For solar heating, it is necessary to find the average heating requirement per hour. This is accomplished by first finding how much heat your house requires per degree day and then multiplying that result by the degree days per season in your area. Proceed as follows:

First, multiply the total hourly heat loss by 24. Then, divide by the temperature factor found in Part 1. This is the BTU's lost per degree day. Next, look up in Table I the number of degree days for your city and write this down in the appropriate space on the work sheet. Now, multiply the degree days by the loss per degree day and you have found the total heat loss per year for your house.

For our Ayer's Cliff example, we have 21,971 BTU's/hour X 24 hours = 527,304. This result divided by 80 = 6,591 BTU's/degree day. From Table I we find that Ayer's Cliff (Rock Island on the table) has 9,000 degree days per year and so, our Ayer's Cliff house uses 9,000 X 6,591 = 59,319,000 BTU's/year.

Nearly all of this requirement is used during the heating season. So, to find the DAILY heating requirement, divide the yearly heating loss (BTU's/year) by the number of heating days per year. For our Ayer's Cliff example, let's assume the heating season lasts 300 days. We divide 59,319,000 by 300 which equals 197,730 BTU's per day which, divided by 24 equals 8,239 BTU's per hour.

NICHOLSON SOLAR ENERGY CATALOGUE

Applying Collector Efficiency To The Ayer's Cliff House

B.T.U. loss per year	59,319,000
192 sq. ft. solar collector X 100,000 B.T.U.'s	− 19,200,000
B.T.U.'s required from conventional sources	40,119,000

This would indicate that the solar system will provide slightly more than 32% of the total heat requirement for the house on an annual basis.

Note: Our experience actually indicates that a much higher percentage is being realized. The monitoring of Solar VI will supply the exact data on which to base calculations. This information will be supplied in future updates to this catalogue.

Solar Use To Maintain Buildings At Temperatures Lower Than 70° F

Installations maintaining lower than normal inside temperatures (i.e. warehouses, seasonal dwellings, etc.) can obtain a much higher percentage of the heating load from the solar system due to the following factors:

1.   Lower building temperatures = lower B.T.U. heat losses.

2.   Lower building temperatures = increased capacity to recover heat from storage. When the building is maintained at 70° F, the heat stored at temperatures below 70° F is unrecoverable. There is a greater amount of heat stored below 70° F (unusable) than there is stored above 70° F (usable).

3.   Lower storage temperatures = increased capacity to transfer heat absorbed by the collector. Low grade heat collected from overcast skies plus a higher percentage of the high grade heat from sunny skies can be stored. (Note that varispeed fans are also a factor. See Section 5.)

NICHOLSON SOLAR ENERGY CATALOGUE

A Nicholson Discourse

Due to the lack of precedent, care must be taken when calculating the efficiency of solar systems.

Misconception is fostered in some instances by the use, out of context, of % solar heat supplied or storage expressed in days. For example, a Professor of Engineering from a University in Ontario was quoted as having stated that a solar system will supply four days of heat during a non-solar period. This statement tells us absolutely nothing. It is analogous to saying, "10 gallons of fuel oil will heat a house for four days". A moments thought will give rise to the question, "four days at what outside temperature?" During a cold spell, the 10 gallons may last only one day and conversely, during a warm spell, it might last a month!

Percentage of heat supplied can be equally misleading. A brief example using hypothetical situations would be:

	living area	insulation	configuration	collector size	% solar heat supplied
home #1	2000 sq.ft.	good	one level	500 sq.ft.	50%
home #2	2000 sq.ft.	poor	one level	500 sq.ft.	35%
home #3	2000 sq.ft.	good	two levels	500 sq.ft.	60%
home #4	2000 sq.ft.	good	one level	250 sq.ft.	25%

Note: This example is given to illustrate a point and should not be taken literally.

In all of these cases, the efficiency of the solar collector is the same. This establishes that percentage of heat supplied is not an indicator of solar system efficiency, unless it is indexed to the size of the collector and the heat loss for a given installation.

Hopefully, when the question "What percentage of heat do you get from your solar system?" is asked to determine efficiency, it will be replaced with the question, "How many B.T.U.'s will your system deliver for a given solar radiation period". The monitoring of solar systems in Canada by the National Research Council will be instrumental in this regard.

NICHOLSON SOLAR ENERGY CATALOGUE

A very rough rule of thumb, for use in areas with approximately 7,000 F degree days per year, 1 square foot of collector will provide the equivalent of the potential heat contained in 1 gallon of fuel oil or 100,000 B.T.U.'s. Since almost 500 gallons of fuel oil was used each season in our Ayer's Cliff house example, this means that roughly 250 square feet of collector would provide about 50% of the heating load.

Also note that storage design has a significant effect on this aspect of system efficiency. (See Section 4.)

Special Note

Local weather conditions, use patterns, furnace efficiency and many other factors can have a great influence on the maximum heating requirement, the average heating requirement and fuel use. This method seeks only to provide a rough estimate of the heating requirement in order to find the approximate requirement to be met by solar energy.

Solar heating to be economical by 1980: study

By TOM RAUM
Associated Press

WASHINGTON — Solar energy will be the cheapest way to warm homes and heat water in many parts of the nation by 1980, a study prepared for a congressional committee concludes.

And the study says that solar heat will be economically more practical in colder northern portions of the United States before it is in the sun belt states.

Prepared by a computer research team at the University of New Mexico, the report was released Saturday by the House-Senate Joint Economic Committee. It says solar heating will be cheaper than either gas or oil by 1980 in Minnesota, North Dakota, South Dakota, Wyoming, Wisconsin, New York, Rhode Island, Massachusetts, New Hampshire, Vermont and Maine.

BY 1985, it will be the cheapest form of home heating in Idaho, Utah, California, Colorado, Nebraska, New Mexico, Iowa, Missouri, Illinois, Michigan, Ohio, Pennsylvania, Delaware, Virginia and Maryland, the study adds.

The study says it now costs about $1,350 to install a solar space heating system in the average new home and about $4,200 to equip the average old home for solar heat.

"Solar feasibility begins in the northern tier of states and with very few exceptions systematically moves southward," the study says. It lists two main reasons:

✔ Heating requirements in the South are less than in the North, so it will take longer for a solar heating system, with its high initial installation cost, to pay for itself, despite abundant amounts of sunshine in many southern areas.

✔ Conventional fuels are generally more expensive in the North than in the South, where they are produced. This will be especially true if Congress lifts the federal price limits that now apply to natural gas shipped in interstate pipelines, the study notes.

Sen. Hubert H. Humphrey, D-Minn., vice chairman of the joint committee, said the University of New Mexico analysis has "convinced me that the federal government should temporarily subsidize the installation of solar energy equipment in homes and offices."

CALCULATION SHEET

Part 1

Thermostat _____ less
Design Temperature _____ (from Table I)
= _____ Temperature Factor

Part 2 INFILTRATION LOSS

	Windows & Doors	H (ft)	W (ft)	Area (sq ft)	Perimeter (lin ft)	Infiltration Factor (from Table II)	Infiltration Loss
S WALL							
W WALL							
E WALL							
N WALL							

Total Infiltration Loss _____

Part 3 CONDUCTION LOSS

	H	W	Gross Area	less Windows & Doors	Net Area	Heat Loss Factor (from Table III)	Heat Loss
S WALL							
W WALL							
E WALL							
N WALL							
CEILING (roof)							
FLOOR							
WINDOWS							
DOORS							

Total Conduction Loss _____
plus Infiltration Loss _____
Total Heat Loss (BTU's/hour) _____

Part 4 AVERAGE HEATING REQUIREMENT

_____ X 24 divided by _____ = _____
Total Heat Loss   Temperature Factor   BTU's/Degree Day

_____ X _____ = _____
BTU's/Degree Day   Degree Days (from Table I)   Loss in BTU's/Year

_____ divided by _____ divided by 24 = _____
Loss in BTU's/Year   Days of   Average Loss
                          Heating Season   Per Day

NICHOLSON SOLAR ENERGY CATALOGUE

CALCULATION SHEET

Part 1 Ayer's Cliff House

Thermostat __70__ less
Design Temperature __-11__ (from Table I)
= __81__ Temperature Factor * *for convenience* __80__

Part 2 INFILTRATION LOSS

	Windows & Doors	H (ft)	W (ft)	Area (sq ft)	Perimeter (lin ft)	Infiltration Factor (from Table II)	Infiltration Loss
S WALL	#1	3	2	6	10	75	750
W WALL	#1	4	2	8	12	75	900
E WALL	#1	2	4	8	12	75	900
	#2	3	6	18	18	75	1,350
N WALL	#1	3	2	6	10	75	750
	#2	3	8	24	22	75	1,650
	door	7	3	21	20	160	3,200

Total Infiltration Loss __9,500__

Part 3 CONDUCTION LOSS

	H	W	Gross Area	less Windows & Doors	Net Area	Heat Loss Factor (from Table III)	Heat Loss
S WALL	4	24	96	6	90	7	630
W WALL	10	16	160	12	148	7	1,036
E WALL	10	16	160	26	134	7	938
N WALL	8	24	192	51	141	7	987
CEILING (roof)	20	20	400	—	400	7	2,800
FLOOR	16	20	320	—	320	5	1,600
WINDOWS	—	—	—	—	70	52	3,640
DOORS	—	—	—	—	21	40	840

Total Conduction Loss __12,471__
plus Infiltration Loss __9,500__
Total Heat Loss (BTU's/hour) __21,971__

Part 4 AVERAGE HEATING REQUIREMENT

__21,971__ X 24 divided by __80__ = __6,591__
Total Heat Loss · Temperature Factor · BTU's/Degree Day

__6,591__ X __9000__ = __59,319,000__
BTU's/Degree Day · Degree Days (from Table I) · Loss in BTU's/Year

__59,319,000__ divided by __300__ divided by 24 = __8,239__
Loss in BTU's/Year · Days of Heating Season · Average Loss Per Day

NICHOLSON SOLAR ENERGY CATALOGUE

ADDITIONAL MATERIALS

Other and more detailed methods of calculating heat loss may be found in the following publications:

ASHRAE HANDBOOK OF FUNDAMENTALS   (Chapters 25, 26 and 27)

CLIMATIC INFORMATION FOR BUILDING DESIGN IN CANADA, National Research Council

MECHANICAL AND ELECTRICAL EQUIPMENT FOR BUILDINGS, by McGuiness & Stein

NICHOLSON SOLAR ENERGY CATALOGUE

TABLE I

DESIGN DATA FOR SELECTED LOCATIONS IN CANADA

Province	City	Design Temperature	Approximate degree days F° per year
Quebec	Sherbrooke	−13	8490
	Montreal	−10	8203
	Quebec	−13	8937
	Baie Comeau	−16	10400
	Chicoutimi	−20	10104
	Coaticook	−12	9194
	Hemmingford	− 9	8400
	Lachute	−13	8900
	Magog	−12	8680
	Rock Island	−11	9000
	Shawinigan	−15	9380
	Valleyfield	− 9	8300
	Victoriaville	−14	9250
British Columbia	Courtenay	18	6000
	Vancouver	19	5515
	Victoria	23	5579
	Williams Lake	−23	9300
Alberta	Banff	−22	10551
	Jasper	−28	10112
	Medicine Hat	−26	8852
Saskatchawan	Hudson Bay	−33	11842
	Prince Albert	−35	11630
	Saskatoon	−30	10856
	Moose Jaw	−27	9894
Manitoba	Churchill	−38	16728
	Portage La Prairie	−22	10800
	Boissevain	−24	10269
	Winnepeg	−25	10679
Ontario	Ajax	− 2	7500
	Armstrong	−38	12458
	Aurora	− 4	7900
	Barrie	− 9	8200
	Brampton	0	7721
	Burlington	3	6800
	Cornwall	− 9	8200
	Forest	6	7031
	Gananoque	− 7	7800

NICHOLSON SOLAR ENERGY CATALOGUE

TABLE I (con't)

Province	City	Design Temperature	Approximate degree days F° per year
Ontario	Hamilton	3	6821
	Kingston	- 7	7724
	Kitchener	1	7566
	Markdale	- 3	8600
	Port Stanley	6	7000
	St. Catharines	5	6537
	Sault St. Marie	-15	9500
	Toronto	1	6827
New Brunswick	Alma	- 5	8400
	Fredericton	-10	8671
	Moncton	- 7	8711
	Saint John	- 7	8453
Prince Edward Island	Charlottetown	- 3	8486
	Souris	- 1	8400
	Summerside	- 3	8440
Newfoundland	Argentia	5	8440
	Gander	- 1	9254
	Goosebay	-25	11887
	Labradore City	-32	14200
	St. Johns	6	8991

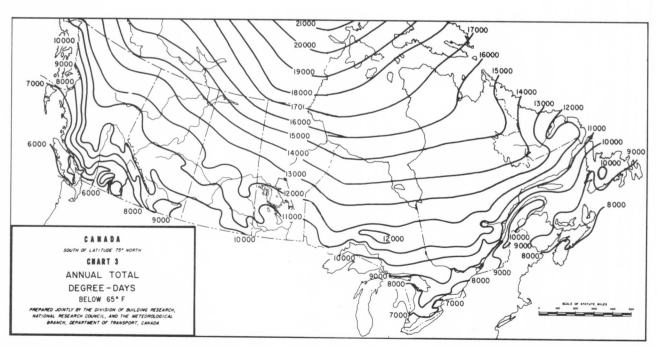

CANADA
SOUTH OF LATITUDE 75° NORTH
CHART 3
ANNUAL TOTAL
DEGREE-DAYS
BELOW 65° F
PREPARED JOINTLY BY THE DIVISION OF BUILDING RESEARCH, NATIONAL RESEARCH COUNCIL, AND THE METEOROLOGICAL BRANCH, DEPARTMENT OF TRANSPORT, CANADA

SCALE OF STATUTE MILES

NICHOLSON SOLAR ENERGY CATALOGUE

TABLE II - INFILTRATION LOSS FACTOR

WINDOWS	40	50	60	65	70	75	80	85
				TEMPERATURE FACTOR				
double hung wood sash (weather stripped)	17	20	25	28	30	32	34	36
double hung metal sash (weather stripped)	25	30	35	37	40	45	50	55
casement windows	35	45	55	60	65	70	75	80
DOORS								
all types with or without storm sash	80	100	120	130	140	150	160	170

TABLE III - HEAT LOSS FACTOR OF HOUSES

WALLS

wood siding - above grade								
tar paper, wood sheathing, lathe, 3 1/2" insulation	4	5	5	6	6	7	7	8
same, no insulation	10	13	15	16	18	19	20	21
tar paper, wood sheathing 1/2" insulation board	8	10	11	12	13	14	15	16
brick - 8"								
bare wall	20	25	30	33	35	38	40	43
brick, furring, lathe plaster	12	15	18	20	21	233	24	26
brick, furring, lathe 1/2" insulation, plaster	9	11	13	14	16	17	18	19
concrete block - 8"								
block, furring, lathe, plaster	13	16	19	21	22	24	26	27
block, furring, lathe 1/2" insulation, plaster	10	12	14	16	17	18	19	20
DOORS								
1 1/2"	20	25	30	32	35	37	40	43
with metal storm door	13	16	20	21	23	24	26	28

NICHOLSON SOLAR ENERGY CATALOGUE

TABLE III CONTINUED	40	50	60	65	70	75	80	85
BASEMENT FLOOR								
concrete slab	2	21/2	3	5	7	8	10	12
with 1" insulation	1	11/4	2	3	4	4	5	6
CEILING WITH ATTIC								
unfloored, ventilated no insulation	24	30	37	40	43	46	49	52
unfloored, unventilated no insulation	14	18	21	22	24	26	27	29
floored, unventilated no insulation	9	11	13	14	15	16	17	18
floored, unventilated 3 1/2" insulation	3	4	4	5	6	7	7	8
floored, unventilated 6" insulation	2	2	3	3	3	3	4	4
cathedral (exposed) 6" insulation	3	4	4	5	6	7	7	8
BASEMENT WALLS								
8" concrete, below grade	2	2	3	3	4	4	5	5
8" concrete, above grade	28	35	42	46	49	53	56	60
SUNWALL								
I	16	20	24	26	28	30	32	34
II	13	16	19	21	22	24	26	27
III	10	13	16	17	18	19	21	22
WINDOWS								
single glass	45	56	68	73	79	85	91	96
single with storm windows	22	27	34	37	40	43	45	48
insulating glass, 1/4" air	26	32	39	42	45	48	52	55

NICHOLSON SOLAR ENERGY CATALOGUE

SOLAR ENERGY TRANSMITTANCE (%) *

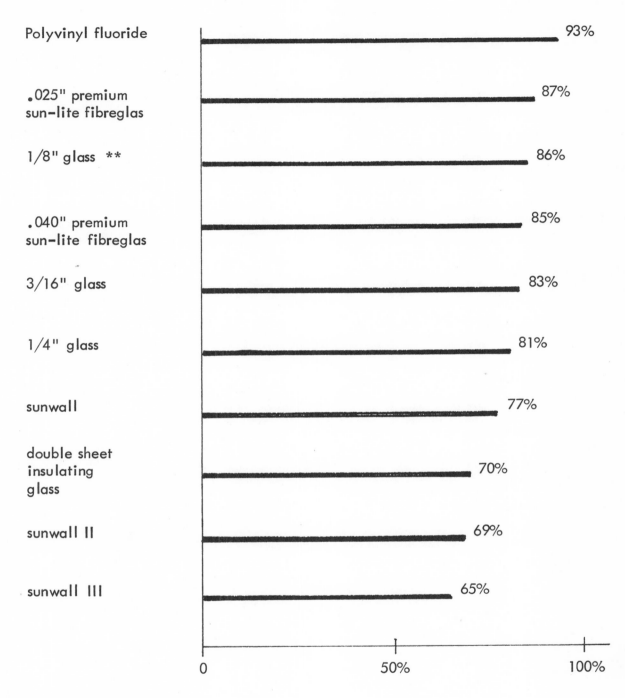

Material	Transmittance
Polyvinyl fluoride	93%
.025" premium sun-lite fibreglas	87%
1/8" glass **	86%
.040" premium sun-lite fibreglas	85%
3/16" glass	83%
1/4" glass	81%
sunwall	77%
double sheet insulating glass	70%
sunwall II	69%
sunwall III	65%

0   50%   100%

*   ASTM E-424

** double strength 'B' grade (DSB)

NICHOLSON SOLAR ENERGY CATALOGUE

NICHOLSON SOLAR ENERGY CATALOGUE

SECTION 3

SOLAR AIR SYSTEMS

SOLAR I

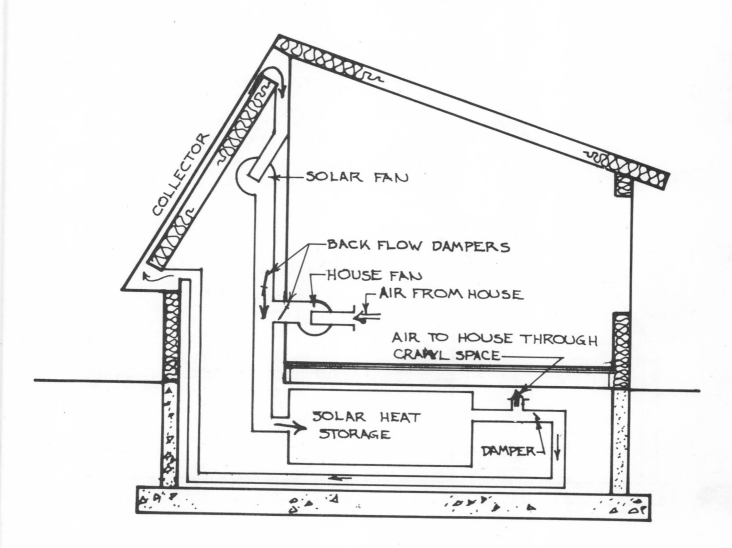

COLLECTOR

SOLAR FAN

BACK FLOW DAMPERS

HOUSE FAN

AIR FROM HOUSE

AIR TO HOUSE THROUGH CRAWL SPACE

SOLAR HEAT STORAGE

DAMPER

Solar I has a two fan parallel flow solar heating system. To collect, the damper opens and the solar fan forces air from the collector into the store where it passes through the damper back to the collector. To heat while collecting, the house fan draws air from the house and forces it through the store and then back to the house. To heat only, the damper closes and effectively isolates the collector from the rest of the system. The house fan operates as before.

Two back flow dampers on the effluent side of both fans prevent short circuiting of either the collecting or house heating air stream while either of these fans are not operating.

The wood stove and the base-board back-up heaters are independent of the solar heating system.

NICHOLSON SOLAR ENERGY CATALOGUE

SOLAR II

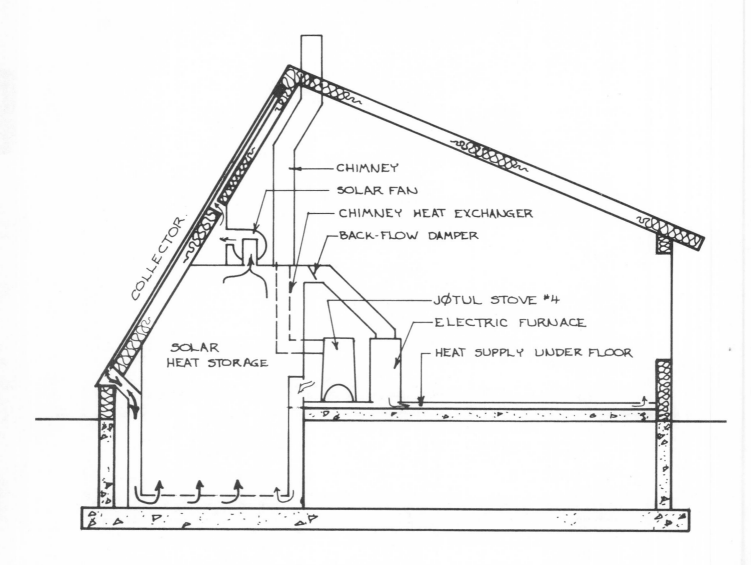

CHIMNEY
SOLAR FAN
CHIMNEY HEAT EXCHANGER
BACK-FLOW DAMPER
COLLECTOR
JØTUL STOVE #4
ELECTRIC FURNACE
HEAT SUPPLY UNDER FLOOR
SOLAR HEAT STORAGE

Solar II has a two fan parallel flow heating system. To collect, the solar fan exhausts the storage and feeds air to the collector. The air returns from the collector to the bottom of the store. To heat while collecting, the fan in the electric furnace draws air from the top of the storage and feeds it to the house via underfloor ducts. House air returns to the bottom of the store. To heat only, the fan in the electric furnace draws air from the storage and feeds the house. If the air supplied to the furnace is not warm enough, the furnace resistance heater activates automatically. A back-flow damper prevents the solar fan from bypassing the heat storage through the electric furnace and the house. A back-flow damper in the feed to the solar fan serves the same purpose for the electric furnace fan. Excess heat from the wood stove is transferred to the heat storage by imbedding a heavy steel section of chimney in the rocks.

NICHOLSON SOLAR ENERGY CATALOGUE

SOLAR III

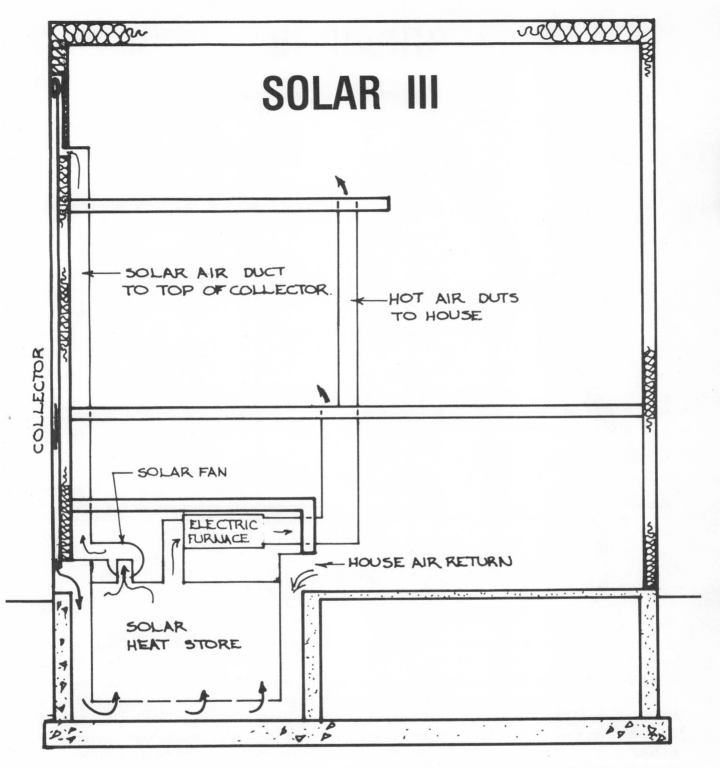

SOLAR AIR DUCT TO TOP OF COLLECTOR.

HOT AIR DUTS TO HOUSE

COLLECTOR

SOLAR FAN

ELECTRIC FURNACE

HOUSE AIR RETURN

SOLAR HEAT STORE

Solar III has a two fan parallel flow system. As in Solar II, air for both collecting and house heating is drawn from the top of the heat storage and returned to the bottom. The electric furnace resistance heater operates automatically only if the air fed to the furnace is not warm enough for house heating. The wood stove is independent of the solar heating system.

3—3

NICHOLSON SOLAR ENERGY CATALOGUE

SOLAR IV

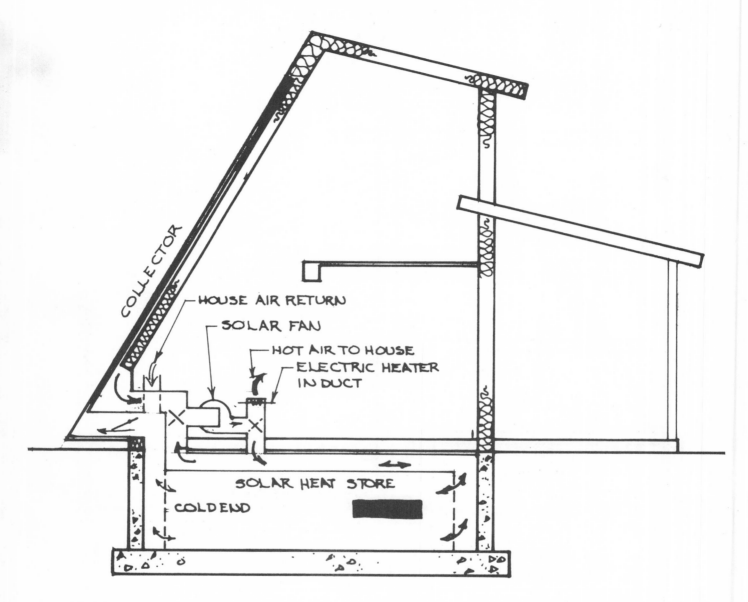

COLLECTOR

HOUSE AIR RETURN

SOLAR FAN

HOT AIR TO HOUSE

ELECTRIC HEATER IN DUCT

SOLAR HEAT STORE

COLD END

Solar IV has a one fan, reverse flow system with two power dampers and one back flow damper. To collect solar heat, the dampers operate to guide air from the collector to the fan and then to the storage. To heat while collecting, the damper in the fan outlet operates to feed air to the house, directly from the collector. To heat only, the dampers operate to feed air from the store to the fan and then to the house. Air for house heating flows through the storage in the opposite direction to air for solar heat collecting. The electric resistance back-up heater is installed in the duct feeding air to the house. It operates automatically only when the air fed to it is not warm enough for house heating. The wood stoves operate independently of the solar heating system. A separate duct system transports warm air from the top of the house to the lower levels.

NICHOLSON SOLAR ENERGY CATALOGUE

SOLAR V

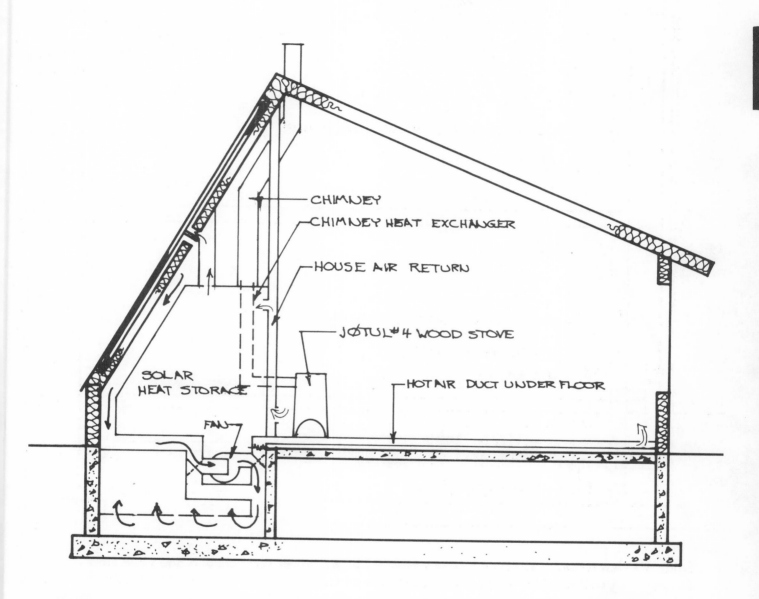

CHIMNEY

CHIMNEY HEAT EXCHANGER

HOUSE AIR RETURN

JØTUL #4 WOOD STOVE

HOT AIR DUCT UNDER FLOOR

SOLAR HEAT STORAGE

FAN

Solar V has a one fan, reverse flow system. House heating and heat storage occur as in Solar IV. Excess heat from the wood stove is transferred to the heat storage by imbedding a heavy steel section of chimney in the rocks.

NICHOLSON SOLAR ENERGY CATALOGUE

SOLAR VI

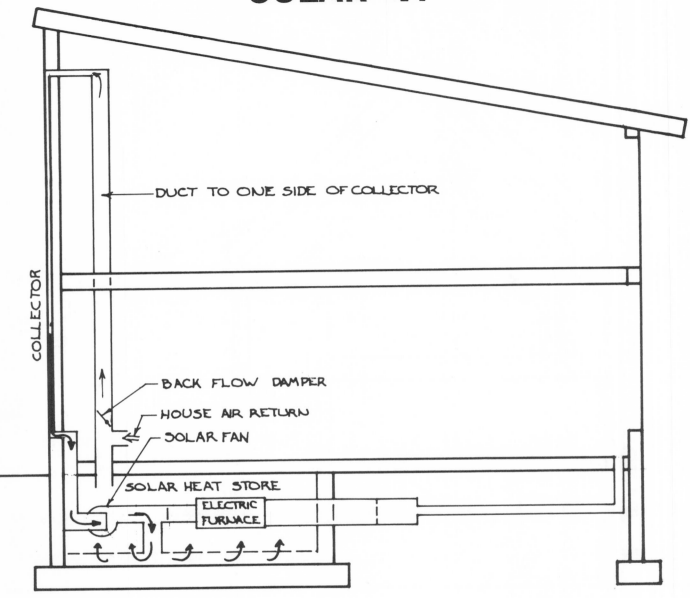

DUCT TO ONE SIDE OF COLLECTOR

COLLECTOR

BACK FLOW DAMPER

HOUSE AIR RETURN

SOLAR FAN

SOLAR HEAT STORE

ELECTRIC FURNACE

Solar VI has a two fan, reverse flow system with two power dampers and one back flow damper. To collect solar heat, the solar system damper opens and then the fan operates exhausting air from the collector and feeding the store. The fan is variable speed, adjusting the rate of air flow to maximize the temperature of the air collected. To heat while collecting, the house damper opens and the house fan heats the house directly from the collector. To heat only, the solar damper and fan are closed and the house damper and fan are open. The house fan draws air from the store and feeds it to the house. The back flow damper prevents the house fan from drawing air from the collector at the house air return. The air for house heating moves through the storage in the opposite direction to the air for solar heat collecting.

3—6

SOLAR VII

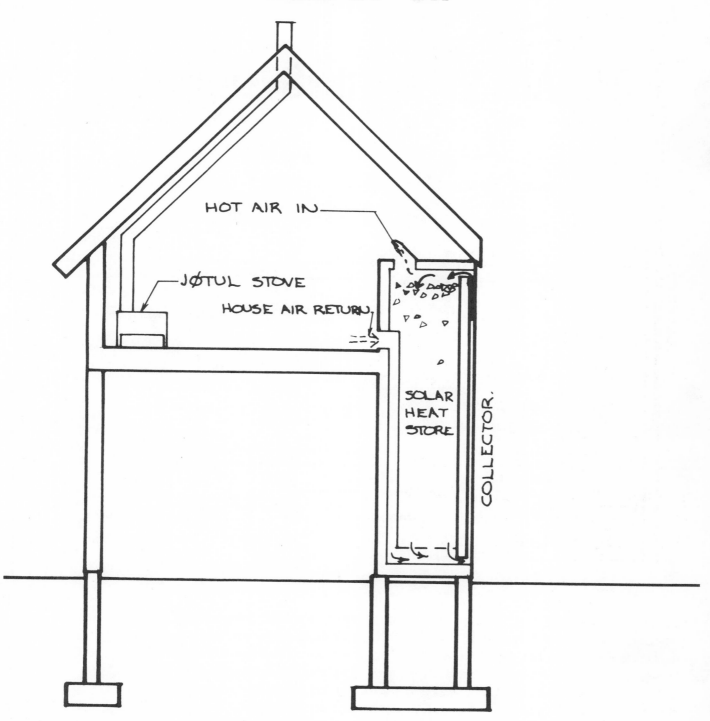

HOT AIR IN

JØTUL STOVE

HOUSE AIR RETURN

SOLAR HEAT STORE

COLLECTOR.

Solar VII has a passive system. Hot air from the top of the collector circulates through the rocks in the heat storage by thermosiphon action. To heat the house, the manual dampers are opened permitting hot air from the store to rise into the house and house return air to flow to the bottom of the store, again by thermosiphon action.

3—7

NICHOLSON SOLAR ENERGY CATALOGUE

SOLAR VI WIRING DIAGRAM

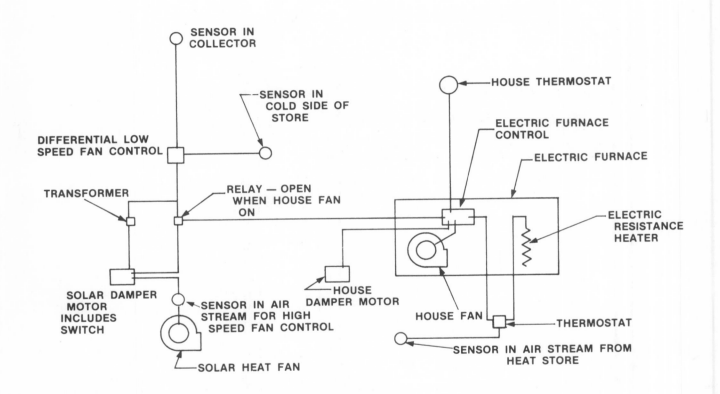

NICHOLSON SOLAR ENERGY CATALOGUE

SOLAR VI - OPERATION OF CONTROLS

1. COLLECTION - When the temperature at the top of the collector is 4° F greater than the cold end of the store, the variflow controller opens the collector damper. When the damper is nearly full open, the auxiliary switch closes and the collector fan will start at minimum speed, delivering about 900 cfm. As the temperature difference increases, the fan speed increases. At 24° difference, the flow rate will be about 1500 cfm.

2. HEATING THE HOUSE - The house fan and heating element are part of a standard electric furnace in which the controls have been slightly modified. When the house thermostat closes, the damper is opened and the fan starts. The electric heating element will only turn on if the temperature switch senses that the air temperature at the fan section is too cool for comfortable heating.

3. SIMULTANEOUS COLLECTION AND HEATING - Both systems operate simultaneously as above causing the air flow to by-pass the store and circulate through the house.

The system is completely automatic, requiring no control by the resident at any time. He only sees a normal house thermostat.

NICHOLSON SOLAR ENERGY CATALOGUE

SOLAR VI CONTROL SYSTEM

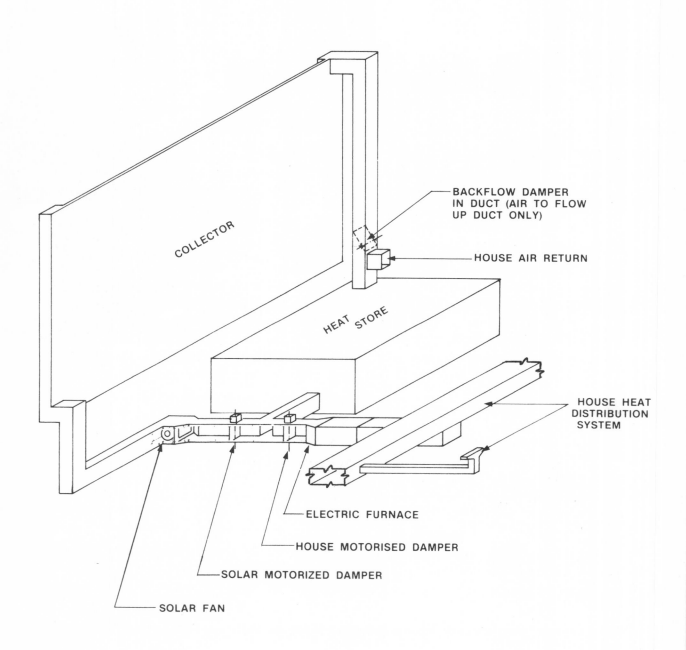

COLLECTOR

BACKFLOW DAMPER
IN DUCT (AIR TO FLOW
UP DUCT ONLY)

HOUSE AIR RETURN

HEAT STORE

HOUSE HEAT
DISTRIBUTION
SYSTEM

ELECTRIC FURNACE

HOUSE MOTORISED DAMPER

SOLAR MOTORIZED DAMPER

SOLAR FAN

NICHOLSON SOLAR ENERGY CATALOGUE

Basic Components of Air System for Solar VI

A.   Trolec Back Flow Damper

B.   Nortron Electric Furnace

C.   Differential Controller

D.   Power Damper consisting of Trolec Damper, Honeywell Damper Motor and Transformer

E.   Dayton Variable Speed Blower

NICHOLSON SOLAR ENERGY CATALOGUE

Opening for return air from collector.

Return air duct from collector in place.

Opening for return air to collector from rock store (note sensor).

Return air duct containing back flow damper to collector from rock store in place.

NICHOLSON SOLAR ENERGY CATALOGUE

Top view of return air duct to collector showing back flow damper. Note: due to a last minute substitution, this is not the same model back flow damper as shown in the composite photo on page 3-11.

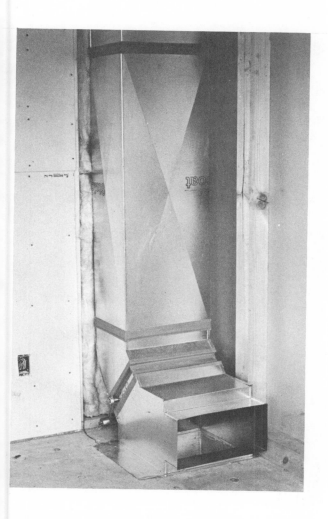

Completed assembly of return air duct to collector from rock store in place. Front opening is the return air inlet from the house.

3—13

NICHOLSON SOLAR ENERGY CATALOGUE

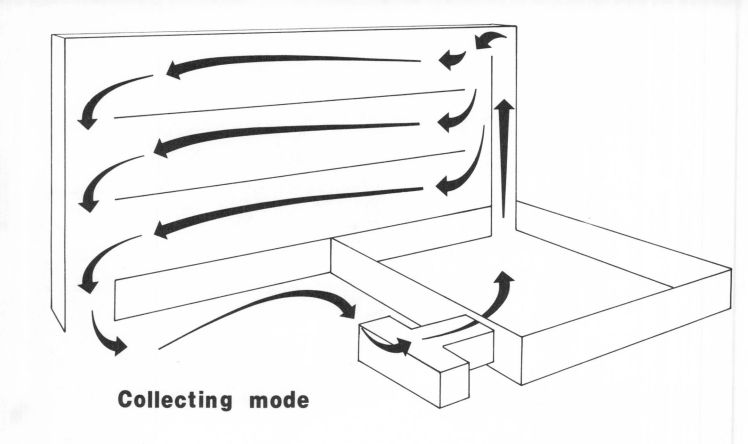

Collecting mode

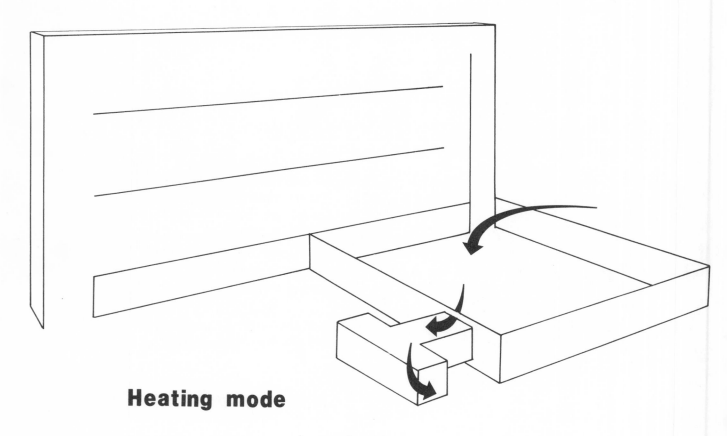

Heating mode

NICHOLSON SOLAR ENERGY CATALOGUE

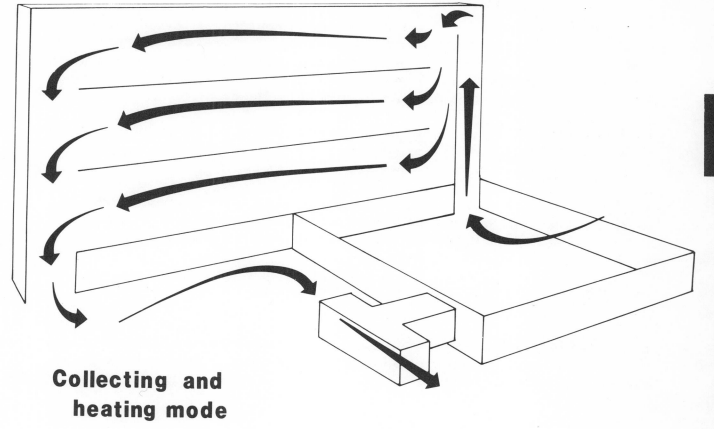

**Collecting and
heating mode**

AIR FLOW IN EVACUATED (FAN DRIVEN) SOLAR SYSTEMS

The principles of lateral air flow through the collector and reverse air flow through the rock store are illustrated in diagrams 1, 2 and 3.

When using forced air, the direction of air flow through the collector has no effect on efficiency. This does not apply to passive systems (see illustration of Solar VII, page 3-7). Passive systems rely on the natural convective characteristics of warm air to initiate thermosyphon action. To accomplish this, the air flow has to be oriented vertically.

In an evacuated (fan driven) system, the fan overcomes the natural convective tendencies of warm air and has the capability to move the air (and the heat it contains) in any direction.

NICHOLSON SOLAR ENERGY CATALOGUE

The advantage of using lateral flow lies mainly in convenience. In several of the Ayer's Cliff solar installations (see pp. 3-2, 3-3, 3-4, 3-5) we have resorted to double back pass collector fabrication in order to place the plenums servicing the collector in a convenient position to facilitate the arrangement of the interior living spaces. In other words, we were trying to hide the collector inlet and outlet ductwork.

The system used in Solar VI simplifies the matter considerably. The air outlet from the collector is completely outside the living space where it serves the double function of solar collector and plenum and only one half of the air supply inlet to the collector is located inside the living space, where it is tucked into a corner. The other half of the air supply inlet to the collector is outside the living space where it serves the double function of solar collector and plenum in the same manner as the air outlet from the collector. The diagrams should help you to understand all these insides and outsides.

AIR FLOW THROUGH THE STORE

The topic of reverse flow vs. parallel flow of the air through the rock store is the subject of much controversy. Set forth in the following text are some of the advantages and disadvantages attached to both systems.

Reverse Flow

Whereby the hot air from the collector enters the rock store at one end and the air supply to the house is taken from the same end. During the collecting mode, the passage of air through the store is in one direction and during the heating mode it is in the opposite or reverse direction.

Lateral Flow

Whereby the hot air from the collector enters the rock store at one end and the air supply to the house is taken from the opposite end. During the collecting mode, the passage of air through the store is in one direction and during the heating mode it is in the same or parallel direction.

Exponents of reverse flow claim, quite rightly, that the reverse flow system maintains one end of the rock store at a higher temperature than the other. The advantages of this temperature differential are:

> Increased efficiency when collecting solar heat due to the lower exit temperatures of the air from the rock store. This enables the circulating air to collect more of the heat absorbed from the sun.

3—16

Increased efficiency of the house heating system due to the higher temperature of the air drawn from the rock store. This is an advantage only when the solar system is installed without the back-up system integrated into the solar heating system. For example, electrical resistance coil baseboard heaters, oil, coal, gas or wood heating devices supplementing the solar heating system without forming part of it. An example of an integrated back up system would be the electric furnace utilized by Solar VI. This furnace supplies the power to circulate the air through the store for both solar heating and conventional heating when the store is depleted.

The disadvantages of a reverse flow system are basically the higher installation cost due to the need for more components to control the air flow and the susceptibility to increased maintenance problems as a result of the increased complexity.

Another point to be considered is that the optimum configuration for a rock store is as close to a cube as possible. A cube has less surface area in proportion to volume contained than a rectangular shape.

On the other hand, a rectangular configuration is optimum for reverse flow. The reason being that the rectangular configuration would allow the air flow to travel a longer distance which in turn maximizes the capability of the system to store heat at different temperatures simultaneously within the rock store.

It would seem that when applying these principles on the small scale occasioned by single family dwellings, the advantages and disadvantages inherent in the rectangular and cube configurations cancel each other out.

Yet to be established by the advocates of reverse flow is exactly how much do we benefit in increased efficiency as compared to the additional installation and maintenance costs added to the solar system.

COLLECTOR FAN CONTROLS

There are three basic controls to activate and deactivate the collector fan during solar and non solar periods. They are called fixed control, differential control and differential control with varispeed output. A fourth control would simply be an on-off switch. This would require the dweller to be on hand at all times. Where this is practical, it should be applied. However, for the purpose of this discussion, we will omit further mention of it.

NICHOLSON SOLAR ENERGY CATALOGUE

For optimum convenience and efficiency, the differential control with varispeed output in conjunction with a speed controllable fan is preferable over the other two choices. However, there are factors that may make an alternate choice more feasible.

First, let's familiarize ourselves with the basic requirements of fan control.

Solar fan must turn on and off during solar and non solar periods.

For optimum performance, the forced air from the fan should be adequate to keep the collector from overheating under a hot sun (resulting in lost heat by reradiation) and not overcool the collector during the beginning and end of a solar period and light overcast days which would reduce the capacity of the system to collect solar heat.

The temperature at which the solar fan is activated and deactivated should always be higher than the temperature of the rock store at the outlet end.

For convenience, the system should be fully automated.

The fixed control in conjunction with a sensor located near the top of the collector turns the solar fan on and off automatically at a predetermined setting. Hence, if the temperature of the store is 80° F, the control would be set at a start up temperature of 90° F. As the temperature of the store fluctuates, it would be necessary to adjust the start up temperature accordingly. The alternative would be to always have the control set at a high setting and accept the reduction in efficiency due to the fan being stopped prematurely. The advantage of using a fixed control is lower initial cost.

The differential control serves the same function as the fixed control with the addition of the differential feature. The differential feature utilizes two sensors. One sensor is located near the top of the collector and the second sensor is located in the air stream leaving the rock store.

These sensors monitor the difference in temperature between the rock store and collector which enables the differential control to turn the collector fan on and off at a temperature 10° F higher than the rock store. This feature eliminates the need to manually adjust the control as the rock store temperature fluctuates.

NICHOLSON SOLAR ENERGY CATALOGUE

The differential control with varispeed output functions in the same manner as the differential control but has the added capacity to vary the speed of the solar fan. This control can only be used with a fan utilizing an adjustable speed motor.

The purpose of all this is to gain control over the air passing through the collector in order to maximize efficiency. Intense insolation (full sun) requires a greater volume of air through the collector to carry away the greater amount of heat absorbed from the sun. On the other end of the spectrum, less intense insolation (hazy skies) demands a lower volume of air through the collector in order to maintain the collecting air temperature at a level higher than the rock store temperature. The varispeed regulates the air flow to maintain the collecting air temperature at a fairly steady 10° F higher than the rock store temperature regardless of the solar conditions.

Keeping in mind that of the percentage of heat contained in the heated air stream coming from the collector, only the portion represented by the differential between the store temperature and air stream temperature multiplied by the volume of air can be placed in storage.

Taking an extreme example to illustrate the point, if you have 1,000 cubic feet of air at a temperature of 80° F as well, you will not capture any of the heat contained in the air stream. By lowering the volume of air to say, 600 cubic feet which, in turn would raise the temperature to say 95° F and then passing it through the same rock store, you would then capture the heat represented by the differential of 15° F.

MISCELLANEOUS NOTES

Motorized dampers are expensive, use them sparingly.

Air control sensors should monitor the temperature of the air stream. Place them accordingly, exposed to the air stream and not, for example, on the collector plate. The ideal place for the collector sensor is up high, near the point where the air leaves the collector.

The ideal place for the storage sensor is at the point where the air stream leaves the rock store on its way back to the collector.

NICHOLSON SOLAR ENERGY CATALOGUE

Consider the impact on efficiency when tempted to use cheaper controls. You rarely get something for nothing, unless you are very, very clever.

Keep it simple . . .

Dayton Variable Speed Blower

. . . but not always.

MODEL # H-1500
THE ACTOVATOR

The H-1500 Actovator control is a low voltage controlled solid state switch to power auxiliary equipment in a solar system.

Typical Applications:

- Auto drain control for thermo-siphon solar systems as freeze protection (solenoid valves)
- To power a small heating element in a solar collector as frost protection.
- Switching unit to shift the output of a solar system from one storage tank to another at a predetermined temperature.
- Switching unit to turn on an auxiliary heating element to maintain a minimum temperature in a solar storage tank.
- To switch a solar home heating system from solar to conventional auxiliary heating at a predetermined temperature.
- Let your ingenuity be your guide.

Features:

- Low voltage control 5.1 VAC maximum short circuit current 4 ma.
- Output may be selected for 120 VAC power normally on or off.
- Controller power requirement 4 watts, 117 VAC, 60 HZ.
- Light emitting diode power on indicator.
- 4 amp. (480 watt) controlled output.
- Sensor activates or deactivates circuit by shorting.

MODEL # H-1503
FIXFLO CONTROLLER

The Model #H-1503 Fixflo controller is a versatile solid state differential temperature control with the following features:

- 4 amp. (480 watt) controlled A.C. output.
- Positive on/off action for pump, relay or solenoid control (no chatter) no oscillation.
- +16°F turn on differential, +3°F turn off.
- Linear control from 30° – 220°F.
- Sensor voltage 8.3 VDC maximum short circuit current 4.15 ma.
- Low power requirement 4 watts, 120 VAC.
- Upper temperature limit control—stops pump circulation with a storage tank temperature of 165°F optional with added sensor.
- Frost cycle—starts pump circulation with a collector plate temperature of 35°F and will continue to circulate water from the storage tank until the plate temperature reaches 45°F, then stops and repeats this cycle as often as required to hold the collector above freezing. (Note: not recommended in areas where very frequent freezing conditions occur). Optional with special sensor.

MODEL # H-1504
FIXFLO CONTROLLER WITH ACTOVATOR

The Model #H-1504 is identical to the #H-1503 Fixflo controller, with the addition of the features of the Model #H-1500 (the Actovator). In this unit, the normally on or normally off A.C. power is controlled by a normally open or normally closed sensor.

MODEL #H-1505
FIXFLO CONTROLLER WITH DUAL OUTLET

The Model #H-1505 is identical to the #1503 with the addition of an auxiliary (dual) outlet which may be used to power two pumps, one on either side of a heat exchanger, or operate a relay or solenoid valve.

MODEL # H-1510
VARIFLO CONTROLLER

The Model #H-1510 is a versatile solid state differential temperature controller with a variable flow rate feature.

This controller must be used with a pump that is speed controllable. The following pumps have been tested and found to perform well with the Model #H-1510 control.

March Model 821BR and 809
Teel Model 1P761* and 1P760
Sundstrand Model LA4302*
Grundfos Model UPS20-42F* and UP25-42S

Note: *Cast iron pump housing. Do not use for direct circulation of domestic water.

The March Model 809 and Teel Model 1P760 pumps are not recommended for use with the Model #H-1510 control, even with a single panel installation, as their flow rates are already too low; thus, there is no advantage to speed control of these pumps. However, they do speed control, and may fit a special requirement.

The Model #H-1510 is a true differential temperature controller. The flow rate (speed) of the pump is controlled by the amount of differential. A very slow flow rate is started with a 3 - 4°F differential and is increased to full pump flow when a 23 - 24°F differential is reached.

3—21

THE ADVANTAGES OF AUTOMATIC FLOW RATE CONTROL ARE MANY

1. The proper flow rate through the solar collector is automatically adjusted based on the amount of energy to be gained, holding plate temperatures down and increasing overall system performance.

2. Eliminates frequent pump cycling, thus extending pump life.

3. All recommended pump motors operate at lower temperatures throughout their speed control range, extending expected pump life.

4. Only the energy required for efficient system operation is used resulting in a power savings.

5. System installation cost is lowered by eliminating the plumbing bypass around the pump commonly used to adjust for a desired flow rate.

6. The proper flow rate is automatically established, eliminating time-consuming bypass adjustments.

The #H-1510 Variflo control also offers upper temperature limit and frost cycle features as explained in the last 2 items of the #H-1503 with the optional sensors.

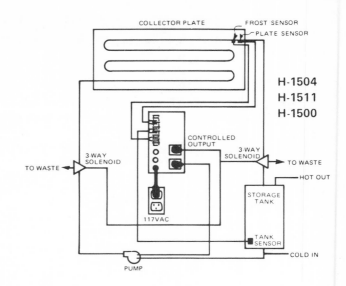

H-1504
H-1511
H-1500

MODEL # H-1511
VARIFLO CONTROLLER WITH ACTOVATOR

The #H-1511 Variflo control is identical to the #H-1510 with the addition of the features of the Actuator Model #H-1500. In this unit, the normally on or normally off A.C. power is controlled by normally open or normally closed sensors.

MODEL # H-1512
VARIFLO CONTROLLER WITH DUAL OUTLET

The Model #H-1512 Variflo controller is identical to the Model #H-1510 with the addition of an auxiliary A.C. outlet (dual outlet), which may be used to power two pumps, one on either side of a heat exchanger. (Note: This auxiliary outlet is also speed controlled and is not suitable for relay or solenoid valve control).

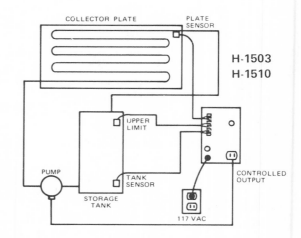

H-1503
H-1510

MODEL # H-1530
RELAY PACKAGE

The #H-1530 is an accessory for Models #H-1503 and #H-1500 controllers, extending output load capabilities to 1 h.p.

A must if pump motor has high starting current or running current above 4 amps.

The relay package comes complete with conduit mounting and A.C. line cord for connection to the controller.

SENSORS

#H-1525   Standard thermistor sensor 10K ohm at 25°C, 1% curve matched.

OPTIONAL ACCESSORIES

#H-1514   Upper temperature limit 85°F. Pool
#H-1515   Upper temperature limit 165°F. Hot water.
#H-1520   Frost cycle sensor with thermistor 35°F.
#H-1535   Mounting Plate
#H-1540   Rain-tite Cover

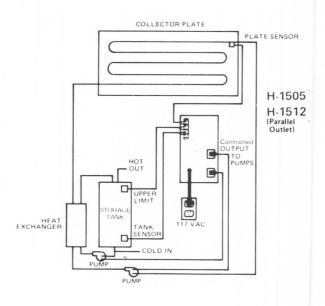

H-1505
H-1512
(Parallel Outlet)

3—22

F SERIES FURNACE

Ideal for standard size installations. CSA approved for zero clearance to combustible materials. With the addition of a cooling cabinet this Series will handle up to four tons of air conditioning. Equipped with high density fibreglass acoustical and thermal insulation.

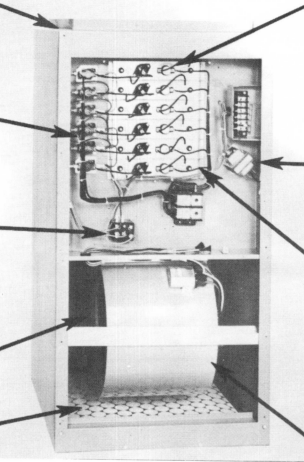

**F SERIES FURNACE
10 THROUGH 30 KW**

CABINET
Steel with baked enamel finish. Approved for zero clearance . . . . . install against combustible surfaces with complete safety.

Size 20″ x 20″ x 39″

TIME DELAY SEQUENCERS
One for each element. Silently turn on elements at staged intervals to prevent power surges that might dim lights or blow fuses.

COOLING FAN RELAY
Standard equipment. Allows continuous fan operation if desired or automatic dual speed control for heating and cooling.

MOTOR
Multi-speed motor is standard equipment. Permanently lubricated.

FILTER
20″ x 20″ x 1″ disposable type. Traps dust and lint. Since no smoke or soot is produced filter life is longer.

SAFETY LIMITS
For absolute safety each element is equipped with two high temperature limits. The primary re-setting type prevents operation at unsafe air temperatures due to blocked or dirty filters. The secondary (back-up) limit is for maximum protection.

TRANSFORMER
Heavy duty 24 volt output is standard in every furnace.

ELEMENT BANK
Nickel-chrome elements give extremely high thermal efficiency. Greater heating surface offers rapid heat transfer. Furnace designed so elements do not glow red . . . . "black heat" indicates lower element temperatures and longer life. Each module slides out if service required.

BLOWER
Rubber mounted and precision balanced for truly quiet operation.

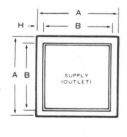

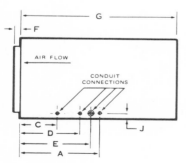

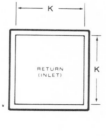

	A	B	C	D
INCHES	20	17	9-1/8	14-1/4
CM	51	43	23	36

E	F	G	H	J	K
17-3/8	1	39	1-1/2	19/16	18
44	2.5	99	3.8	4	46

NICHOLSON SOLAR ENERGY CATALOGUE

INSTALLS ALMOST ANYWHERE . . . . In a basement, closet, crawl space or any unused area or alcove. CSA approved for "Zero" clearance so there is no need to leave wasted space between the furnace and combustible surfaces.

EFFICIENCY . . . . No chimney is required so 100% of the heat produced stays inside the building. The use of a two-stage thermostat improves efficiency even more by using only part of the furnace's heating capacity on warmer days.

SIMPLE INSTALLATION . . . . No complex controls to attach. Just connect power and thermostat wires.

CLEANLINESS . . . . No soot or smoke produced.

VERSATILITY . . . . Add air conditioning, a power humidifier, electronic air cleaner as desired for complete home comfort.

QUIET OPERATION . . . . The blower is the only moving part and it is especially mounted and balanced for quiet running.

MULTI-SPEED MOTOR . . . . Standard equipment for versatility and convenience.

F SERIES

240 VOLT — SINGLE PHASE

MODEL NO.	FURNACE KW	AMPS*	H.P.	MIN. WIRE SIZE CU	MIN. WIRE SIZE AL	BTUH	BLOWER SIZE
21 F 10	10	46.0	1/4	4	3	34100	9 x 7
21 F 15	15	66.8	1/4	4	2	51195	9 x 7
21 F 20	20	86.4	1/3	2	1/0	68250	10 x 8
21 F 25	25	107.2	1/3	1/0	2/0	85325	10 x 8
21 F 30	30	128.1	1/3	2/0	4/0	102390	10 x 8

208 VOLT — SINGLE PHASE

MODEL NO.	FURNACE KW	AMPS*	H.P.	MIN. WIRE SIZE CU	MIN. WIRE SIZE AL	BTUH	BLOWER SIZE
81 F 9	9	48.0	1/4	4	3	30700	9 x 7
81 F 13	13.5	69.6	1/4	3	2	46075	9 x 7
81 F 18	18	90.1	1/3	2	1/0	61430	10 x 8
81 F 22	22.5	111.8	1/3	1/0	3/0	76790	10 x 8
81 F 27	27	133.4	1/3	2/0	4/0	92150	10 x 8

208 VOLT — THREE PHASE

MODEL NO.	FURNACE KW	AMPS*	H.P.	MIN. WIRE SIZE CU	MIN. WIRE SIZE AL	BTUH	BLOWER SIZE
83 F 12	12	38.0	1/4	6	4	40950	9 x 7
83 F 13	13.5	42.2	1/4	6	4	46075	9 x 7
83 F 24	24	70.2	1/3	2	1/0	81910	10 x 8
83 F 27	27	78.5	1/3	1	1/0	92150	10 x 8

*MOTOR AMPS INCLUDED: 240V—1/4 H.P. 4.3A   1/3 H.P. 3.1A
208V—1/4 H.P. 4.7A   1/3 H.P. 3.6A

LF SERIES

240 VOLT — SINGLE PHASE

MODEL NO.	FURNACE KW	AMPS*	H.P.	MIN. WIRE SIZE CU	MIN. WIRE SIZE AL	BTUH
21 LF 25	25	108.3	1/2	1/0	3/0	85325
21 LF 30	30	129.1	1/2	2/0	4/0	102390
21 LF 35	35	149.3	1/2	3/0	250	119455
21 LF 40	40	170.8	1/2	4/0	300	136520

208 VOLT — SINGLE PHASE

MODEL NO.	FURNACE KW	AMPS*	H.P.	MIN. WIRE SIZE CU	MIN. WIRE SIZE AL	BTUH
81 LF 30	30	148.8	1/2	3/0	250	102390
81 LF 35	35	172.8	1/2	4/0	300	119455
81 LF 40	40	196.8	1/2	250	350	136520

208 VOLT — THREE PHASE

MODEL NO.	FURNACE KW	AMPS*	H.P.	MIN. WIRE SIZE CU	MIN. WIRE SIZE AL	BTUH
83 LF 25	25	74.0	1/2	4	2	85325
83 LF 30	30	87.9	1/2	2	1/0	102390
83 LF 35	35	101.9	1/2	1	2/0	119455
83 LF 40	40	115.9	1/2	1/0	3/0	136520

*MOTOR AMPS INCLUDED: 240V—4.1A
208V—4.8A

MOTOR HP	SPEED	BLOWER SIZE	MAX CFM AT VARIOUS ESP IN. H2O 0.3	0.4	0.5
1/4	LOW	9 x 7	1000	954	912
1/4	HIGH	9 x 7	1181	1113	1040
1/3	LOW	10 x 8	1120	1084	1054
1/3	MED	10 x 8	1291	1241	1175
1/3	HIGH	10 x 8	1540	1476	1399
1/3	*LOW	10 x 8	1179	1139	1096
1/3	*MED	10 x 8	1364	1327	1272
1/3	*HIGH	10 x 8	1636	1586	1525

*High velocity permanent type filter used

MOTOR HP	SPEED	BLOWER SIZE	MAX CFM AT VARIOUS ESP IN. H2O 0.3	0.4	0.5
1/2	LOW	12 x 11	1400	1375	1350
1/2	MED	12 x 11	1800	1750	1700
1/2	HIGH	12 x 11	2150	2130	2110

TEMPERATURE RISE FOR ALL MODELS

TO DETERMINE TEMPERATURE RISE USE FOLLOWING EQUATION USING CFM AT DESIRED ESP.

$$TR = \frac{KW \times 3413}{1.085 \times CFM}$$

NICHOLSON SOLAR ENERGY CATALOGUE

SECTION 4

COLLECTOR FABRICATION

WEATHERABILITY OF FIBERGLASS SOLAR COLLECTOR COVERS

By James S. White, Product Development Manager, Kalwall Corporation. Mr. White is one of the leaders in research and development of fiberglass reinforced plastics for over 25 years, has been involved in the development of special FRP products for the past 8 years, including the development of the accepted industry testing procedures for load/deflection, shatter resistance and the visual rating system for weathered FRP. Mr. White is a registered professional engineer and an active member of the Society of the Plastics Industries, the Society of Plastics Engineers, American Society for Testing and Materials, Solar Energy Industries Association and the American Society of Heating, Refrigeration and Air-Conditioning Engineers.

Abstract

The objective of this paper is to demonstrate the proper method of evaluating the weatherability of fiberglass solar collector covers and to document the performance after weathering. The following discussion will cover such important features for solar collector covers as solar energy transmission, ultraviolet degradation, thermal degradation, surface erosion, impact resistance and thermal shock.

Three basic types of fiberglass reinforced polyester sheets are considered. The first material (refered to as material # 1) is a proprietary material developed specifically for the solar energy industry by Kalwall Corporation called Sun-Lite Premium. The second material (refered to as material # 2) is Sun-Lite Regular, which is also manufactured by Kalwall Corporation but can be considered an acrylic modified, highly light stabilized polyester. The third material (refered to as material # 3) is a standard grade fiberglass reinforced polyester sheet and is included for the purposes of this bench mark as a comparison.

Solar Energy Transmission

When considering fiberglass reinforced polyester (FRP) for a solar collector cover, one of the most important properties is solar energy transmission. Accurately measuring the solar energy transmission of diffuse materials such as FRP has caused many researchers problems because of the light scattering phenomena. The preferred method of measuring the solar energy transmission of diffuse materials, according to the American Society for Testing and Materials, is ASTM E 424 (Test for Solar Energy Transmittance and Reflectance of Sheet Materials) method "B". This method requires a 28" X 28" sample of the material to minimize the effect of light scattering. Initial solar energy transmission for a "super clear" FRP can run between 80% and 90%.

Method "A" of ASTM E 424 has been used with widely varying degrees of success. Many problems have been encountered because of small samples and the location of the sensing device relative to the integrating sphere surface. However, with proper care, solar energy transmission by wavelength curves can be generated (Fig. 1).

SPECTRAL TRANSMITTANCE SUN-LITE
(Fig. 1)

Fiberglass reinforced polyester has the desirable properties of very high transmission over the typical solar spectrum and near opacity in the longwave range for excellent heat trapping properties.

Ultraviolet Degradation

Degradation due to ultraviolet radiation has long been of great concern to those people designing or using products exposed to sunlight. Researchers in the FRP industry have come a long way in retarding ultraviolet degradation. A typical non-light stabilized, general purpose polyester can lose more than 15% transmission in just 50 hours of exposure to a sun lamp. One of the earliest attempts to improve the UV resistance of polyester was to add ordinary aspirin as a light stabilizing additive. After 50 hours of exposure to a sun lamp, a general purpose polyester will only lose 5% transmission if aspirin is added as a light stabilizer.

Obviously, today's researchers have gone much beyond aspirin in the field of light stabilization. Altering the polyester backbone (modifying the glycols and acids which make up polyester), adding acrylic, adding sophisticated light stabilizers and applying special coatings or films are all necessary to produce a quality solar collector cover.

4—2

In order to facilitate research into UV degradation, several different weatherometers were developed and are in general use today. The most common are the Fluorescent, Carbon Arc and Xenon weatherometers. The Fluorescent weatherometer has a high concentration of UV and causes more severe changes than the Carbon Arc or Xenon weatherometers.

Although it is extremely difficult to correlate weatherometer hours to real time outdoors, many researchers use 250 – 400 weatherometer hours as approximately one year of actual weathering (2,000 hours equals approximately 5 years of real time).

Our samples were exposed in a Fluorescent weatherometer for 2,000 hours. Colour change (E) and light transmission readings were taken at 500 hour intervals.

<u>Colour Change</u> – Measurements of colour change were taken in accordance with the ASTM D 2244 method. After 2,000 hours, material # 1 had a colour change of 3.5. Material # 2 had a change of 10 and depending upon formulation, a standard grade FRP sheet could have a total colour change of around 28 (see fig. 2).

COLOR CHANGE
FLUORESCENT WEATHEROMETER

(Fig. 2)

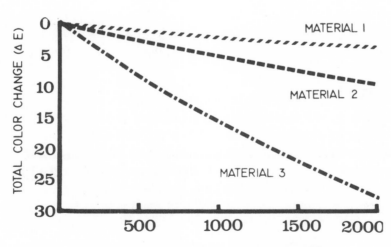

In order to verify the weatherometer results, colour change measurements were taken on a sample of material # 1 weathered in South Florida for 5 years. South facing exposures in South Florida are considered the most severe natural environment in the United States

NICHOLSON SOLAR ENERGY CATALOGUE

because of large quantities of sunlight, heat and moisture. The colour change of material # 1 was found to be 4.4. (A specially coated piece of this same material had a colour change of only 1.1.)

Light Transmission – Light transmission measurements were taken on the same weather-ometer specimens. Material # 1 lost only 3% light transmission after 2,000 hours while material # 2 lost 11%. A standard grade fiberglass reinforced polyester can loose up to 20% light transmission in only 500 hours of exposure time. (Fig. 3)

It is apparent from the above data that it is extremely important to consider the grade of fiberglass reinforced polyester when trying to decrease ultraviolet degradation.

LIGHT TRANSMISSION
FLUORESCENT WEATHEROMETER

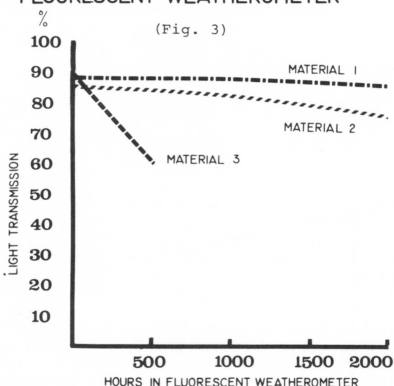

(Fig. 3)

Thermal Degradation

Another area of extreme importance for solar collector covers is thermal degradation. In most efficiently operating flat plate collectors, the cover temperature will not reach above 200° F. Therefore, tests were conducted on samples continuously aged in a 200° F oven for 1 year. The drop in solar energy transmission for both material # 1 and material # 2 was approximately equal (about 10%). However, the standard grade sheet lost more than 50% solar energy transmission in the same 1 year period of continuous exposure (Fig. 4).

4—4

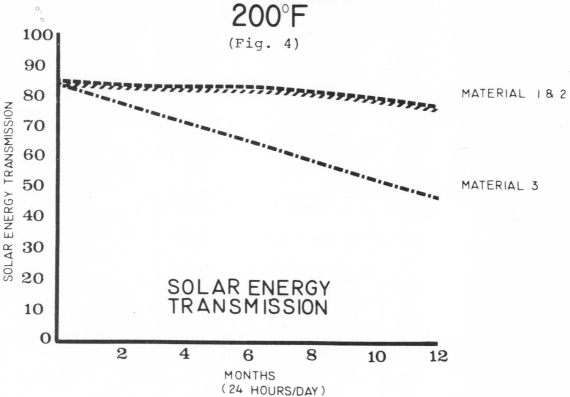

THERMAL DEGRADATION
200°F
(Fig. 4)

MATERIAL 1 & 2

MATERIAL 3

SOLAR ENERGY TRANSMISSION

SOLAR ENERGY
TRANSMISSION

MONTHS
(24 HOURS/DAY)

It is possible for cover plate temperatures higher than 200° F to occur during stagnation in collectors with improperly designed venting systems. Stagnation temperatures occur when no fluid (either water or air) is flowing through the collector. For example, with 300 BTU's per square foot per hour insolation and an outside temperature of 60° F, the absorber plate could reach 380° F and the inner cover of a double cover could reach as high as 260° F

After 300 hours (which is equal to 10 hours per day for 30 days), material # 1 lost only 2% solar energy transmission while material # 2 lost 4%. Extending the test to 5,000 hours, material # 1 lost approximately 10% solar energy transmission at 300° F. Material # 2 lost 22% and a standard grade material lost 40% under the same conditions (Fig. 5).

THERMAL DEGRADATION
300° F
(Fig. 5)

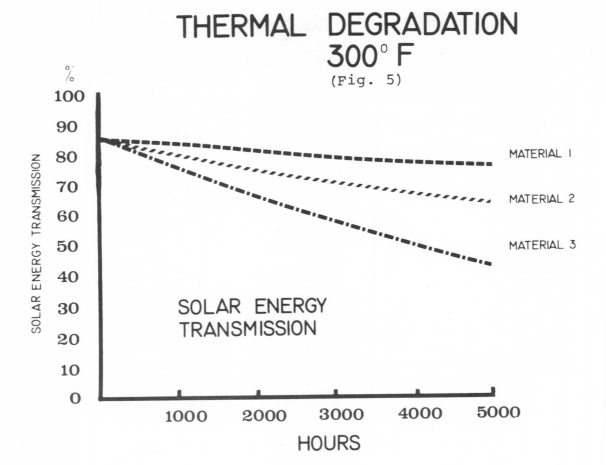

Surface Erosion

One of the weathering factors that is most important in terms of maintenance for long term performance is surface erosion of the collector surface. Surface erosion is the actual physical wearing away and oxidation of the surface. The result is exposed fibers on the surface sometimes called "fiber bloom". In order to measure the amount of surface erosion, measurements were taken with a Clevite 1200 Surfanalyzer. Both average roughness and peak-to-valley roughness were measured.

First we considered the average surface roughness (the average magnitude of all surface irregularities reported in microinches or 1/1,000,000th of an inch). The surface erosion for material # 1 is not noticeable for the first three years of outdoor weathering in South Florida. However, at the end of four years some surface roughness was noticeable and, after five years, there was about 55 microinches of average erosion. A standard grade of fiberglass can have more than 105 microinches of average erosion after only two years of South Florida exposure (Fig. 6). In order to halt this kind of surface erosion, a proprietary high temperature coating manufactured by Kalwall Corporation called Kalwall Weatherable Surface can be applied. After five years of weathering exposure, only 14 microinches (hardly noticeable to the human eye) of average erosion was measured on material # 1 with this coating (material # 1W).

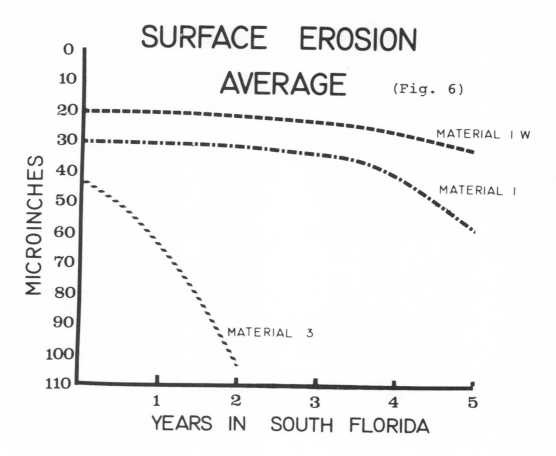

SURFACE EROSION AVERAGE (Fig. 6)

MICROINCHES

MATERIAL 1 W

MATERIAL 1

MATERIAL 3

YEARS IN SOUTH FLORIDA

A more dramatic measurement is of peak-to-valley roughness. Using peak-to-valley measurements instead of average measurements, material # 1 showed a maximum roughness of approximately 300 microinches of change while the coated sample (material # 1W) showed only 100 microinches of change. Both samples had been weathered for five years in South Florida. A standard grade sheet of FRP can have more than 1,000 microinches of erosion after only two years of the same exposure. (Fig. 7).

Impact Resistance

Embrittlement is often of great concern to people using plastics. One of the major reasons fiberglass reinforced polyester is used as a solar collector cover is its remarkable impact strength and shatter resistance. Unlike glass, which can be easily broken into dangerously sharp pieces, fiberglass reinforced polyester is completely shatter resistant. The best way to measure impact resistance for solar collector covers is to use the falling ball method.

NICHOLSON SOLAR ENERGY CATALOGUE

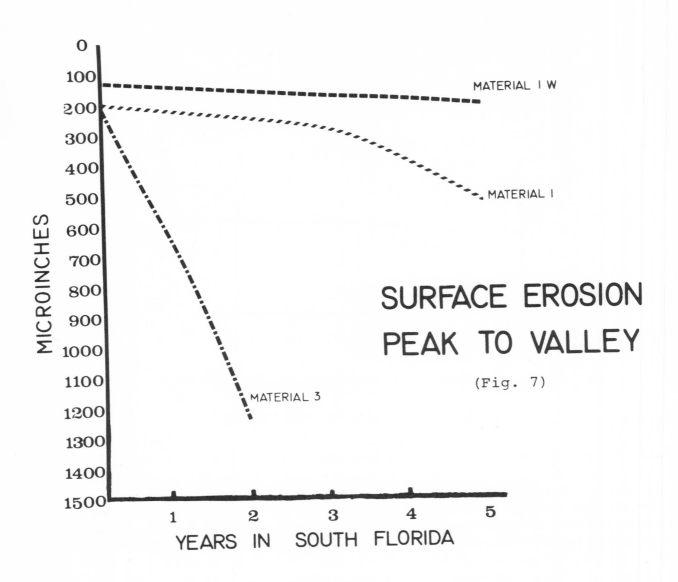

SURFACE EROSION
PEAK TO VALLEY

(Fig. 7)

MICROINCHES — (vertical axis: 0, 100, 200, 300, 400, 500, 600, 700, 800, 900, 1000, 1100, 1200, 1300, 1400, 1500)

MATERIAL I W

MATERIAL I

MATERIAL 3

YEARS IN SOUTH FLORIDA — (1, 2, 3, 4, 5)

To prove fiberglass reinforced polyester does not loose its remarkable impact strength after many years of outdoor exposure, a 14 year old sample was taken from a building and tested. The control (an un-weathered sample) for this test required 25 foot pounds (a 6.4 pound steel ball dropped from 4 feet) to cause a rupture of the material. The 14 year old sample, however, required 32 foot pounds (the same 6.4 pound steel ball dropped from 5 feet) to cause rupture (Fig. 8).

Low temperature impact likewise, does not cause a problem. Tests have been conducted on fiberglass reinforced polyester at $-40°$ F and the results showed almost a 50% increase in the dynamic load required to cause a rupture.

NICHOLSON SOLAR ENERGY CATALOGUE

IMPACT STRENGTH
(SHATTER RESISTANCE)
(Fig. 8)

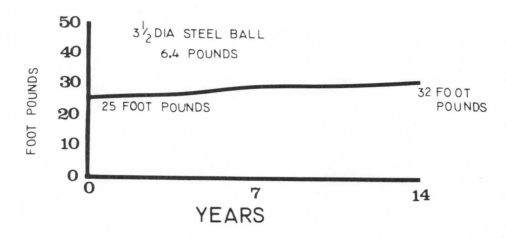

Thermal Shock

The final property to be considered for a solar collector cover to be able to withstand the effects of weathering is thermal shock. Many times during the life of a solar collector, a rain storm or other rapid change in temperature may cause a severe thermal shock to a heated collector. To test fiberglass reinforced polyester's resistance to thermal shock, a sample was heated to 300° F and then quickly submerged in cold water. The thermal shock did not cause any harmful effects or noticeable degradation to the material.

Summary

It has been shown that high grades of fiberglass reinforced polyester exhibit excellent weatherability. Critical properties for solar collector covers such as solar energy transmission, ultraviolet and thermal degradation resistance, erosion resistance, impact resistance, low temperatures and thermal shock have been examined and shown to be highly acceptable for safe and efficient use in the solar industry.

Special thanks are extended to the American Cyanamid Company and Owens-Corning Fiberglas Corporation for their generous technical assistance and testing.

NICHOLSON SOLAR ENERGY CATALOGUE

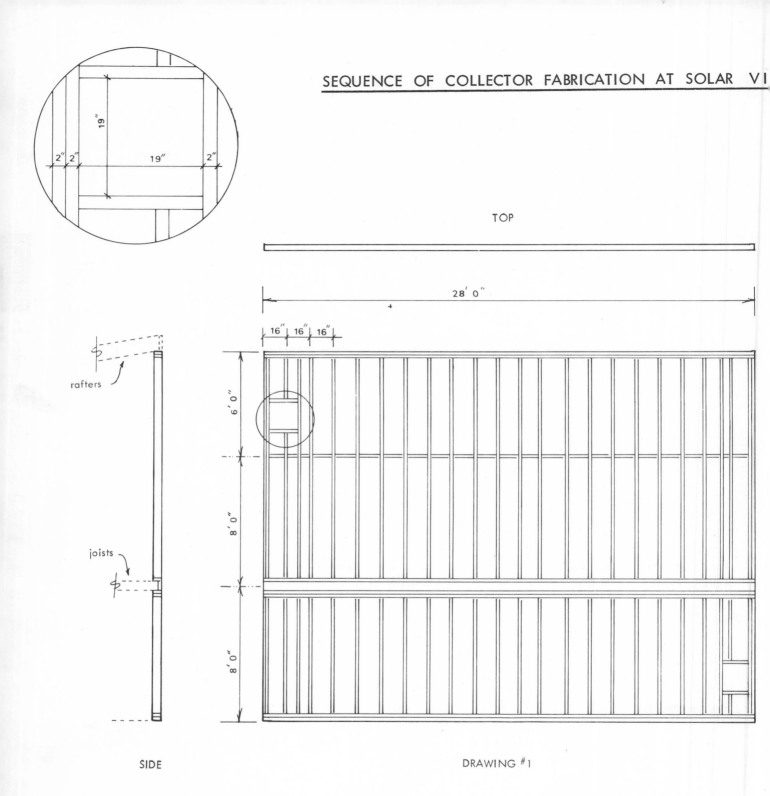

TOP

rafters

joists

SIDE

DRAWING #1

Drawing # 1 illustrates the framing for the south wall.

4—10

The frame assembly lying on the ground corresponds to the lower 8' on drawing # 1.

The technique employed here is standard in the trade and involves framing the wall section on the ground and then raising it into place.

SECTION 4

NICHOLSON SOLAR ENERGY CATALOGUE

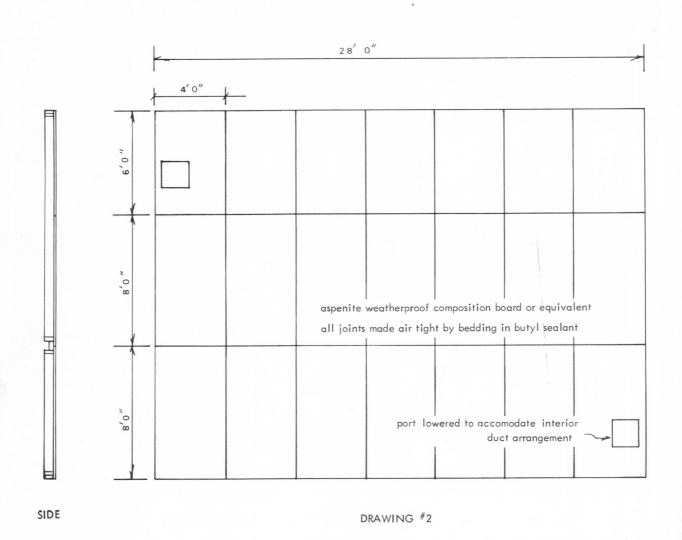

28' 0"

4' 0"

6' 0"

8' 0"

8' 0"

aspenite weatherproof composition board or equivalent

all joints made air tight by bedding in butyl sealant

port lowered to accomodate interior
duct arrangement

SIDE

DRAWING #2

NICHOLSON SOLAR ENERGY CATALOGUE

South wall completed to the stage outlined in drawing # 2. Emphasis should be made to seal all joints.

NICHOLSON SOLAR ENERGY CATALOGUE

TOP

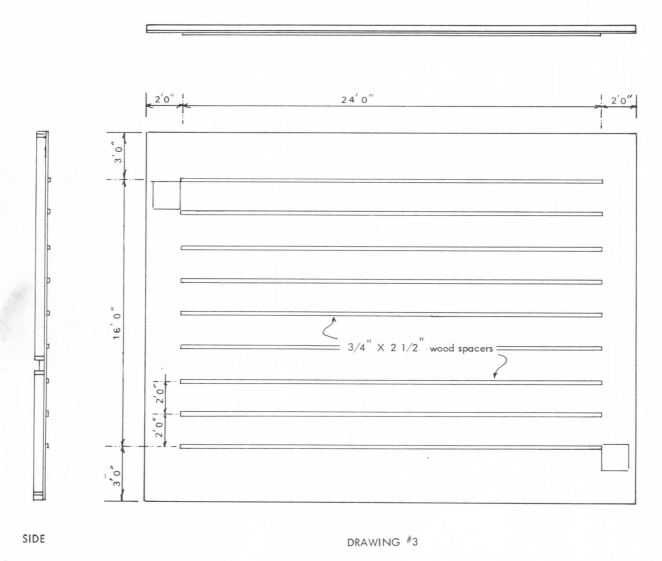

2'0"   24'0"   2'0"

3'0"

16'0"

3/4" X 2 1/2" wood spacers

2'0" 2'0"

2'0"

3'0"

SIDE

DRAWING #3

4—14

Spacing bars in place as shown in drawing # 3.

NICHOLSON SOLAR ENERGY CATALOGUE

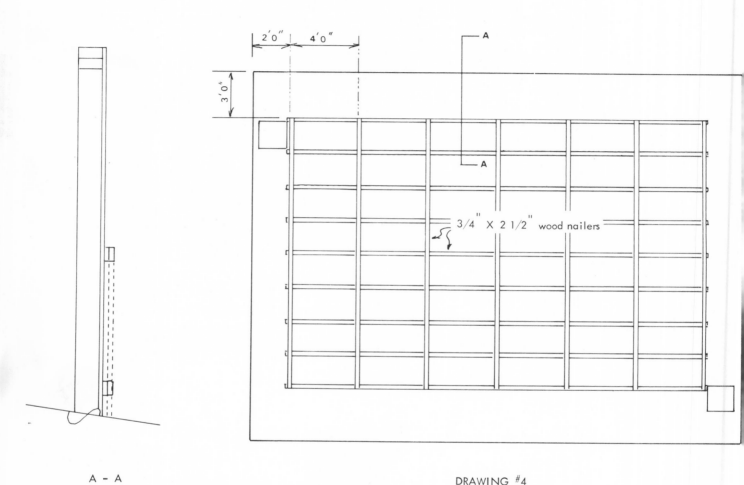

2'0"   4'0"

3'0"

3/4" X 2 1/2" wood nailers

A - A

A

A

DRAWING #4

NICHOLSON SOLAR ENERGY CATALOGUE

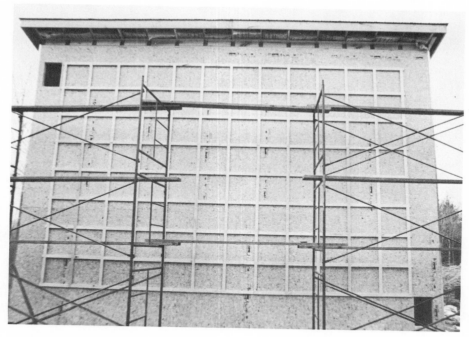

3/4" x 2 1/2" wood nailers in the photograph are on 2' centers.

3/4" x 2 1/2" wood nailers in place as shown in drawing # 4.

Note the air space for the collector heat transfer air stream (arrow).

NICHOLSON SOLAR ENERGY CATALOGUE

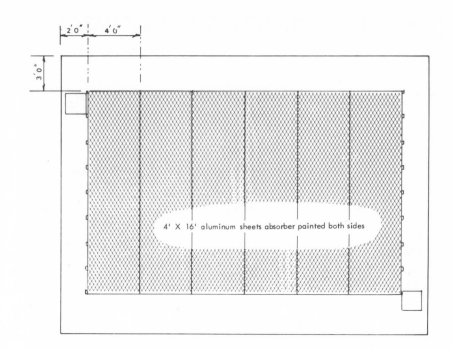

4' X 16' aluminum sheets absorber painted both sides

DRAWING #5

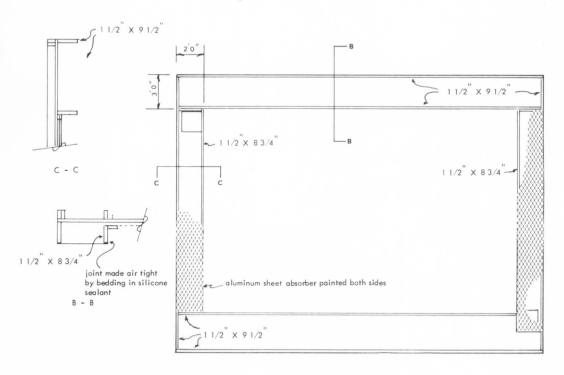

1 1/2" X 9 1/2"

C - C

1 1/2" X 8 3/4"

joint made air tight
by bedding in silicone
sealant

B - B

2' 0"

3' 0"

B

B

1 1/2" X 9 1/2"

1 1/2" X 8 3/4"

1 1/2" X 8 3/4"

C   C

aluminum sheet absorber painted both sides

1 1/2" X 9 1/2"

DRAWING #6

4—18

NICHOLSON SOLAR ENERGY CATALOGUE

1 1/2" x 8 3/4" and 1 1/2" x 9 1/2" framing in place as shown in drawing # 6.
Aluminum absorber plates being placed into position (drawing # 6).

Sealing the absorber plate. The
sealant will be reinforced when
covered with the glazing bars.

Collector turn on sensor located
at the top of the exhaust side of
the collector.

NICHOLSON SOLAR ENERGY CATALOGUE

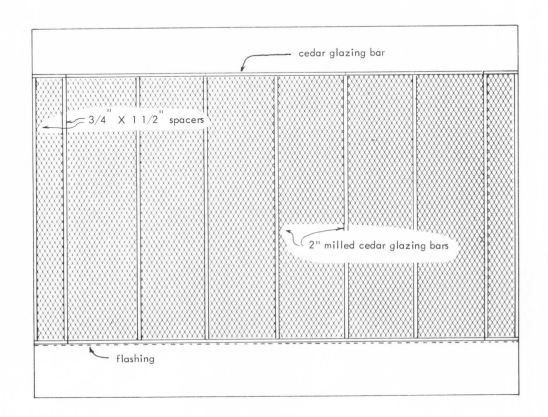

cedar glazing bar

3/4" X 1 1/2" spacers

2" milled cedar glazing bars

flashing

DRAWING #7

Glazing bars in place
as shown in drawing
7. First layer of
Sun-lite fiberglas
reinforced plastic
being applied.

4—21

NICHOLSON SOLAR ENERGY CATALOGUE

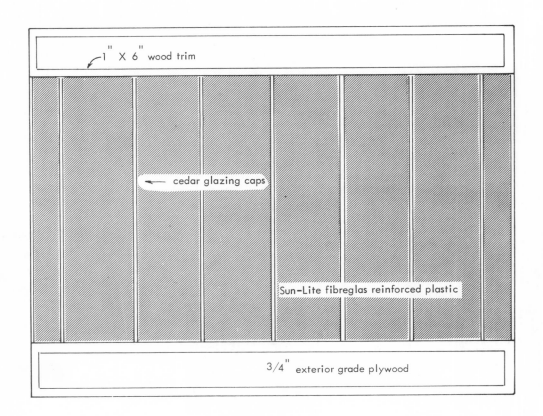

DRAWING #8

NICHOLSON SOLAR ENERGY CATALOGUE

Completed Solar Collector

Absorber Plates

The absorber plates shown in this series are aluminum with an elm leaf green painted surface. The choice of colour, elm leaf green, was based upon a study by the University of Florida showing it to be the optimum colour for efficient solar heat absorption.

Aluminum was chosen for its non-corrosive qualities.

The inherent problem contained in the choice of aluminum is the difficulty involved in painting the surface. There is little doubt that this should be left to professionals. I recommend that the do-it-yourselfer choose either galvanized sheet metal with any of the standard painting processes readily available or purchase his absorber plates pre-coated.

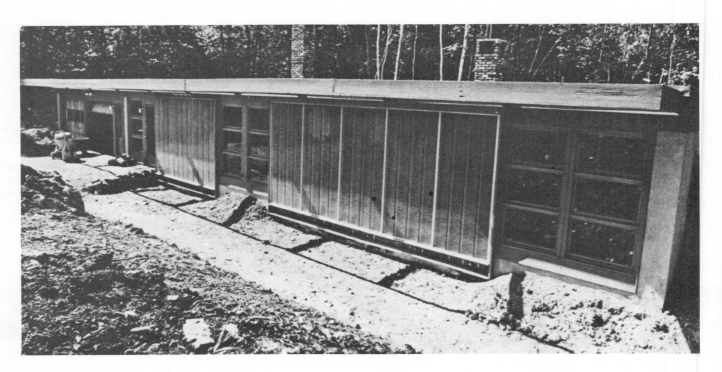

Photos of finished collector installations using Sun-lite fiberglas reinforced plastic by Kalwall Corporation.

4—24

COLLECTOR COVERS

The primary purpose of a collector cover is to permit the sun's rays to enter the solar collector while at the same time trapping as much of the absorbed heat energy inside as possible.

In direct response to the needs of the solar energy industry, Kalwall Corporation has developed single and double layered covers and cover systems. Kalwall's two specially formulated figerglas sheets, Sun-lite Regular and the exclusive Sun-lite Premium offer high performance and low cost.

Sun-lite Collector Cover Sheet

* High Solar Transmittance (85-90%)
* Tough Impact Resistance
* Lightweight
* Easily Cut and Installed
* Low Cost
* Highest Ultra-violet and Heat Resistance of any Fiberglas Reinforced Plastic

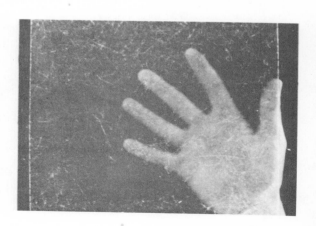

SOLAR I GETS A FACE LIFT

BEFORE: Double glazed collector on Solar I.

In the quest for high quality and low maintenance on our solar collectors, we have opted in the past for double glazed tempered thermopane in conjunction with extruded aluminum pressure caps.

After monitoring several solar installations using Kalwall Sun-lite fiberglass reinforced plastic as the glazing layer and assessing the results of the tests on single vs. double glazing (see design considerations, page 2-6) it was decided to retrofit our solar demonstration home with Sun-lite using curved glazing bars.

Solar VI, the National Research Council demonstration home, will utilize Sun-lite with flat glazing bars.

Pro's and con's of these alternate methods of glazing will be evaluated and made available through the catalogue update service. Results thus far have shown promise that we can expect a sharp reduction in installation costs and less maintenance.

DURING: Glazing bars in place, first layer of Sun-lite in place.

AFTER: Back to work.

NICHOLSON SOLAR ENERGY CATALOGUE

SECTION 5

STORAGE FABRICATION

HEAT STORAGE IN ROCKS

The intermittent availability of solar radiation dictates the need for storing surplus heat for use during non solar periods.

Heat may be stored by raising the temperature of inert substances such as water or rocks. Other systems using reversable chemical reactions are in the developement stage and have no practical application on a cost effective basis at this time.

Water has the capacity to store three times the amount of heat for a given volume as rocks. This requires the rock store to be three times bigger than the water store in order to have the same heat storage capability. The disadvantage of having to build the larger container for the rock store is more than compensated for by the economy, convenience and lack of maintenance associated with air/rock solar systems.

Some of the desireable characteristics of water may be incorporated into the air/rock solar system in a manner that avoids the inherent problems of solar water systems.

Solar X will preheat the water supply by embedding several finned copper heat exchangers and a galvanized iron water storage tank in the rock store. The pre-heated water will then flow to a conventional electric water heater to be raised to the desired temperature for domestic use.

Components of water preheating system to be used in Solar X

Pertinent Factors Concerning Rock Stores

The tortuous path of the air stream through the rock bed ensures efficient heat exchange. Tests at Ayer's Cliff have shown that the temperature of the air stream leaving the pebble bed was never more than 3° F higher than the rock temperature.

NICHOLSON SOLAR ENERGY CATALOGUE

The rocks do not have to be washed. The relatively slow air flow over the rock surface lacks the velocity to dislodge and carry dust particles. For example, Solar I has 192 cubic feet of rock with an estimated 62,000 square feet of surface area. The average air flow of 600 cfm through the system produces an average velocity of only .0096 feet per minute over the rock surface. Along with the above, we have the fact that all of the installations thus far have not required a change of air filters!

Crushed stone or pebbles, 1 1/2" to 2" of a fairly uniform size, has proven suitable for the rock store.

Uncontaminated waste heat from any source can be utilized as an alternate energy source for the rock store. For example, heat can be transfered from a chimney through the use of a heat exchanger. Electricity generated from windmills can also be used to heat a resistance coil placed in the store.

Off peak rated electricity, where applicable, can provide an inexpensive source of heat when applied to a resistance coil located in the rock store.

As the configuration of the rock store approaches a cube, the heat retention efficiency increases due to the increased ratio of volume to surface area. Less surface area for a given volume equals less heat loss or longer storage capacity. This applies to house design as well. Two story squarish houses lose less heat than long, one story houses.

A cubic foot of crushed stone will store approximately 20 BTU's per degree fahrenheit rise.

Be careful of this one: Regarding ratio of collector area to storage volume obtained from averaging out the ratio used in existing systems gives a rule of thumb that defines 1.25 cubic feet of rock to each square foot of collector as being in the ballpark. This information is given to provide a feel for the design considerations involved. The actual ratio can, and should, vary wide from this mark to satisy the varied design requirements occasioned by geographic locations, use, etc. of the solar system. For example, if you have more than one heat source to charge the rock store, it would make sense to enlarge the rock store in relation to the solar collector to accommodate the influx of the extra heat.

Stating that the store should be well insulated and air tight at the joints is self evident. Careful attention should be paid to this, less you create a situation where the house becomes super heated at times causing discomfort and wasting energy. It is analogous to an oil tank leaking its contents on the floor.

NICHOLSON SOLAR ENERGY CATALOGUE

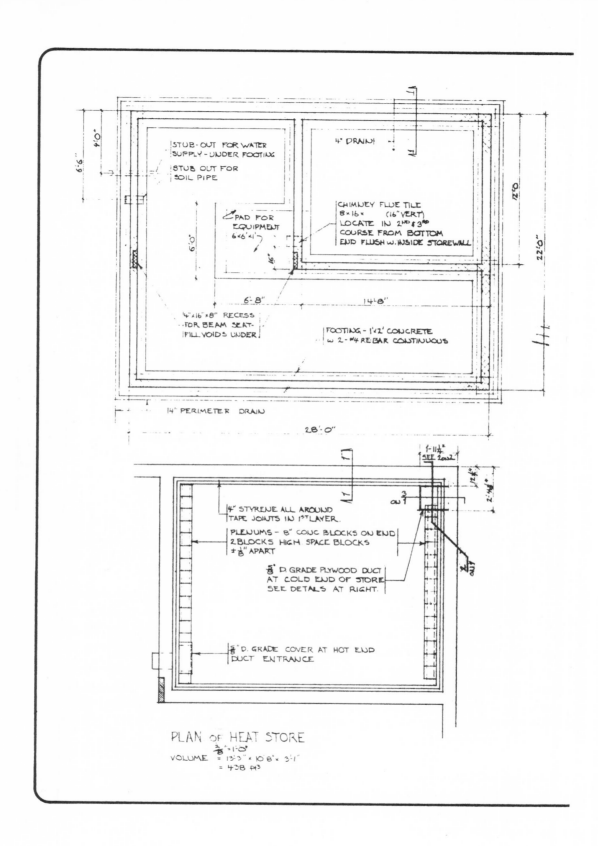

STUB-OUT FOR WATER
SUPPLY - UNDER FOOTING

STUB OUT FOR
SOIL PIPE

4" DRAIN

CHIMNEY FLUE TILE
8×16× (16" VERT)
LOCATE IN 2ND & 3RD
COURSE FROM BOTTOM
END FLUSH W. INSIDE STOREWALL

PAD FOR
EQUIPMENT
6'×6'×1'

4"×16"×8" RECESS
FOR BEAM SEAT-
FILL VOIDS UNDER

FOOTING - 1'×2' CONCRETE
W 2 - #4 REBAR CONTINUOUS

6'-8"   14'-8"

6'-0"

6'-9"

4'-0"

22'-0"

12'-0"

14" PERIMETER DRAIN

28'-0"

4" STYRENE ALL AROUND
TAPE JOINTS IN 1ST LAYER.

PLENUMS - 8" CONC BLOCKS ON END
2 BLOCKS HIGH SPACE BLOCKS
± 3/8" APART

3/8" D. GRADE PLYWOOD DUCT
AT COLD END OF STORE
SEE DETAILS AT RIGHT.

3/8" D. GRADE COVER AT HOT END
DUCT ENTRANCE

1'-11¼"
SEE 2 on 2

PLAN OF HEAT STORE
3/8"=1'-0"
VOLUME = 13'3" × 10'8" × 3'1"
= 438 ft³

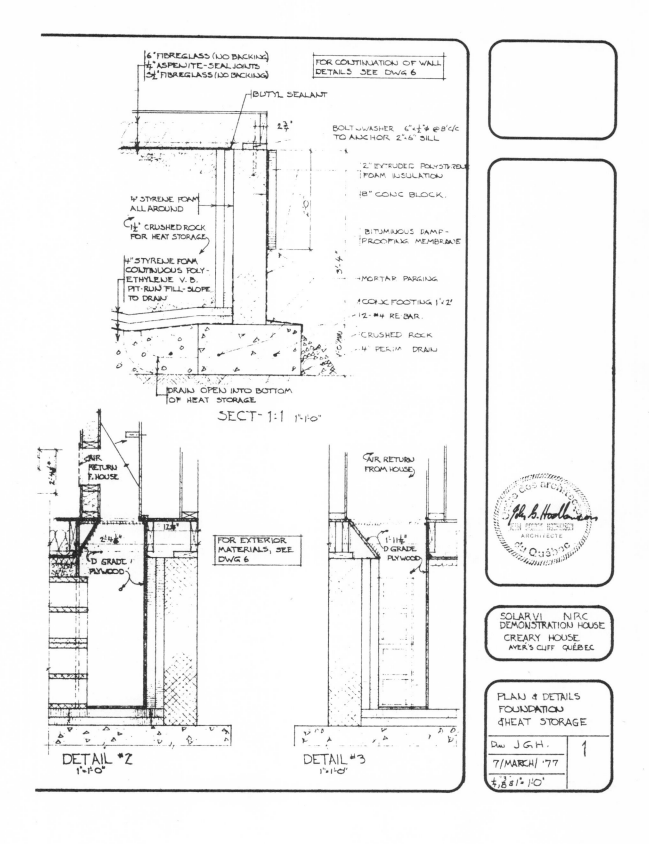

6" FIBREGLASS (NO BACKING)
4" ASPENITE-SEAL JOINTS
3½" FIBREGLASS (NO BACKING)

FOR CONTINUATION OF WALL DETAILS SEE DWG 6

BUTYL SEALANT

2⅞"

BOLT & WASHER 6" x ½" Ø @ 8' c/c TO ANCHOR 2"x6" SILL

2" EXTRUDED POLYSTYRENE FOAM INSULATION

8" CONC BLOCK

4" STYRENE FOAM ALL AROUND

1½" CRUSHED ROCK FOR HEAT STORAGE

4" STYRENE FOAM CONTINUOUS POLY-ETHYLENE V.B. PIT RUN FILL-SLOPE TO DRAIN

BITUMINOUS DAMP-PROOFING MEMBRANE

3'-4"

MORTAR PARGING

CONC FOOTING 1'x2'

12-#4 RE BAR

CRUSHED ROCK

4" PERIM DRAIN

DRAIN OPEN INTO BOTTOM OF HEAT STORAGE

SECT- 1:1 1"=1'-0"

AIR RETURN F. HOUSE

2'-4½"

12½"

2'-4½"

D GRADE PLYWOOD

FOR EXTERIOR MATERIALS, SEE DWG 6

AIR RETURN FROM HOUSE

1'-11½"

D GRADE PLYWOOD

DETAIL #2
1"=1'-0"

DETAIL #3
1"=1'-0"

SOLAR VI NRC
DEMONSTRATION HOUSE
CREARY HOUSE
AYER'S CLIFF QUÉBEC

PLAN & DETAILS
FOUNDATION
& HEAT STORAGE

DW J G H.	1
7/MARCH/ '77	
⅛ & 1"=1'-0"	

NICHOLSON SOLAR ENERGY CATALOGUE

SECTION 6

ALTERNATE ENERGY SYSTEMS

WIND POWER

As the reader passes through this section, he will note the conspicuous absence of wind generated energy systems. We regret this absence.

The reason is simple. We know of no system that has proven itself dependable and cost effective. Hopefully, such a system exists and when we hear of it, we will publish the information in the updates.

In the meantime, we have resisted the impulse to fill up many pages with the same old hackneyed data "just for show".

Ditto for manure power.

6—1

SECTION 6

NICHOLSON SOLAR ENERGY CATALOGUE

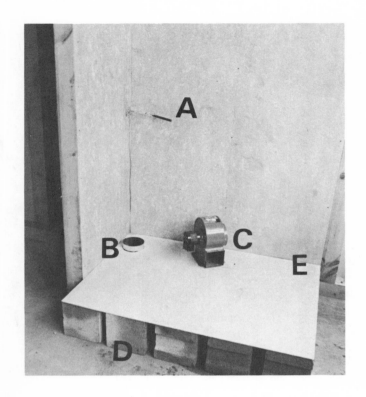

Detail of base for energy

efficient fireplace

Picture 1 illustrates the first step in building a fireplace with improved efficiency.

Picture 2 shows the prefabricated steel firebox in place on a hearth composed of firebricks. All the joints are sealed (arrows) to prevent smoke from escaping.

The next stage in construction will be to enclose the unit with asbestos board.

NICHOLSON SOLAR ENERGY CATALOGUE

Referring to picture 1:

A.   Capillary heat sensor

B.   Duct connecting the air space around the firebox with "C".

C.   The blower (shown here for illustration but actually installed beneath the floor) connected to duct B and the house heating system.

D.   Cement blocks laid sideways with holes aligned. Primary function is to provide a thermal break between the hearth and the wood floor. Holes (not shown) leading into the air spaces in the cement blocks will both cool the space above the wood floor and supply some heat by thermosyphon action.

E.   Asbestos sheet liner covering all surfaces for fireproofing.

The purpose of this design is to enclose an airspace around the firebox. When the firebox is burning, the air around the firebox becomes superheated. The sensor "A" then turns on the blower "C" which evacuates the superheated air surrounding the firebox by pulling it through duct "B" and then transferring it to the house heating system.

Fireplaces tend to be too hot in the immediate vicinity causing the rest of the house to feel cold by comparison. This design distributes the heat uniformly throughout the house, thereby creating a more comfortable atmosphere.

An added feature (to be shown in updates) is the return air vent located at the top of the fireplace next to the roof. This feature enables the system to circulate the hotter air which always collects in the uppermost areas back down to the cellar and then, uniformly throughout the house.

NICHOLSON SOLAR ENERGY CATALOGUE

The last Nicholson non-solar home

Seeing the snow melt over the septic tank
in the front of my own house prompted me
to install the septic tank for Solar II
under the greenhouse in order to utilize
the escaping heat.

CAUTION Be certain that all joints are
well sealed for protection against odors.

6—4

SECTION 7

SOLAR WATER HEATERS

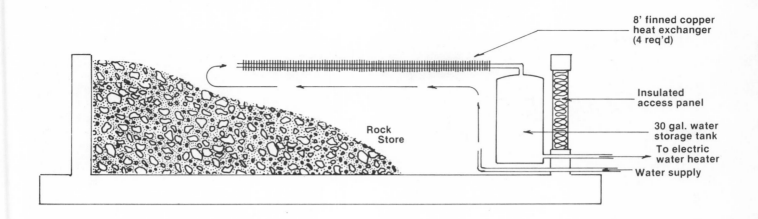

8' finned copper
heat exchanger
(4 req'd)

Insulated
access panel

30 gal. water
storage tank

To electric
water heater

Water supply

Rock
Store

Sketch of water pre-heater installation for Solar X Project

Finned copper heat exchangers and
30 gallon water tank to be used for
Solar X water pre-heater.

NICHOLSON SOLAR ENERGY CATALOGUE

Swimming pool water heater with Sun-lite glazing

Interior view showing Roll-bond copper absorber plate

NICHOLSON SOLAR ENERGY CATALOGUE

"Can I shut it now? I want my pool to heat up."

NICHOLSON SOLAR ENERGY CATALOGUE

SECTION 8

SOLAR HEATED GREENHOUSES

SOLAR POWERED GREENHOUSES

This paper is by Drew A. Gillett of the Solar Components Division of Kalwall Corporation and was presented at the New England Solar Energy Association's 1st Annual Conference on "Decision Making in Solar Technology" in June, 1976.

Introduction

For many years, greenhous heating was merely a question of using enough cheap fuel (wood, coal, oil, etc.) to overcome the large heat losses of a "glass house" at night. With the advent of the small consumer greenhouse with its large surface area to volume ratio and the necessity for low initial and maintenance costs, electric heaters seemed a reasonable alternative. Unfortunately, rapidly increasing electric costs have eaten away most of these savings.

This situation has been coped with primarily by turning back thermostats, shutting down greenhouses in winter or by growing different, more cold-tolerant crops. More creative users have improved insulation through use of inner layers of transparent materials. Several manufacturers now offer inner layer kits or plans. Many owners have simply suspended ordinary polyethelyne sheeting in their greenhouses to form a large insulating dead air space above the plants.

One company, over the last two years, has developed a greenhouse prefabricated with special panels which more than halve the heat loss and consequently the heating costs of conventional glass houses. These savings have made it possible for users to have the same quality plant growth and year-round pleasure for the same operating cost as five years ago. Now, however, in the face of still greater energy costs, something more needs to be done to allow the greenhouse owner to become relatively independent of future price increases. The answer to all of this is solar energy thermal storage.

Thermal storage works as follows: Solar energy, which overheats conventional greenhouses (single and more so on double glazed) and has to be vented (ie. wasted) during the day, is stored in the form of a small temperature rise in a thermal mass (such as barrels or tubes filled with water) thus preventing over-heating. This energy is later released to the greenhouse, resulting in higher average nightime temperatures and reducing the amount of auxiliary heat required.

SECTION 8

NICHOLSON SOLAR ENERGY CATALOGUE

FIGURE I

Solar Greenhouse at New Alchemy Institute
Exterior
showing Kalwall Sun–Lite south wall

FIGURE 2
Interior
Showing Kalwall Sun–Lite–Solar membrane south wall
Insulated reflective north wall and thermal mass.

NICHOLSON SOLAR ENERGY CATALOGUE

Review Of The Literature

Many researchers have investigated the use of thermal storage, improved insulation and specially modified greenhouses for the purposes of reducing conventional energy consumption while improving the plant yield of conventional greenhouses. Among these are T.A. Lawand and others at the Brace Research Institute in Quebec; John Kusianovich with Steve Baer's Zomeworks Corporation in Alburquerque, New Mexico; W.F. Yanda of the Solar Sustenance Project in Santa Fe, New Mexico; Professor Robert T. Nash of the University of Vanderbilt School of Engineering in Nashville, Tennessee; the New Alchemist's Dr. John Todd of Woods Hole, Massachusetts and many others. Most of these researchers have concluded that it is technically feasible to incorporate modifications into conventional and newly designed greenhouses to improve the percentage of their annual heating needs provided by solar rather than conventional energy sources.

In particular, Lawand showed that for conventional greenhouses in Quebec, 13% to 20% of their energy requirements were provided by the sun. By changing the shape of the greenhouse, incorporating reflective insulation on the north side and double layer plastic on the south side, it was possible to raise this percentage to 50% to 60%!

John Kusianovich of Zomeworks Corporation showed that it was possible to keep the lowest temperature in a greenhouse from dropping below 50° F while the outdoor ambient often plunged into the teens. The design incorporated heat storage water tanks and movable foam insulation panels.

Professor Nash made some of the first attempts at quantifying the degree to which the sun's energy can be coupled to the thermal mass; and his experiments carried out in the winter of 1974-5 have enabled this and other researchers to more accurately predict the performance of such thermally massive greenhouses.

Finally, researchers at the New Alchemists at Woods Hole, Massachusetts have constructed a fairly large greenhouse utilizing most of these innovations, including the insulated north wall, changed shape and a highly insulated, yet transmissive south wall (as illustrated in Figures 1 and 2).

Despite the innovations of these researchers and their careful work in the physics or horticulture involved with greenhouses, none have yet combined a commercial consumer greenhouse with the fruits of their research on solar thermal storage. This paper will investigate the possibilities of combining thermal mass in the form of Kalwall's Solar Collector Storage Tubes with various single and double wall greenhouses.

8—3

TABLE I

SUMMARY OF ECONOMIC ANALYSIS

Greenhouse	Square Feet	Basic Electric Consumption (Therms)	# Tubes	Insulation	Final Electric Consumption (Therms)	Cost Of Modification	Payback Yr.
5512 Leanto	65	132	10	No	66	$500	5
8512 Leanto	100	192	10	No	97	450	3.25
8012 Free N-S Standing	96	218	5	Yes	103	286	1.63
8012 Free E-W Standing	96	218	10	Yes	61	567	2.11
8012 Free Standing N-S	96	218	5-5' Tubes	Yes	140	300	2.67
8012 55° Night Setback N-S	96	123	5-5' Tubes	Yes	66	300	3.54

NOTE: ASSUMES;

1) Greenhouse is already a solar collector. What's needed is storage so house can be heated after sun has set.

2) Most efficient storage material is water (holds more heat than rock, picks up and releases heat faster than rock)

3) Sun-Lite fiberglass tubes (12" x 8') with black absorbing coating are most cost effective containers available($27.00/ea. unpacked, F.O.B. Manchester, N. H.) since they combine collection and storage.

4) Examples are based in Boston (6,000 degree days). Heat loss calculations are based on standard ASHRAE methods. Solar gain calculations are based on Kalwall experience with solar battery and solar radiation and cloud cover data from TEA; Solar Energy Home Design in Four Climates.

5) Therm is 100,000 BTU's which is the equivalent of 29.3 kilowatt hours (which is also equivalent to the useful heat of one gallon of fuel oil burned in a typical residence).

6) Pay back calculations very rough as investment figures only approximate. Kilowatt hour rate of $.05 used. Inflation rate of fuel is assumed to equal interest rate on capital.

7) Solar contribution based on A) initial 20% of total heating requirements provided by solar, B) solar battery performance is derated by equivalant 20%.

Economic Analysis

Before embarking on the testing and analysis of a full scale prototype, it was decided that it would be beneficial to perform a preliminary economic analysis of suitably modified greenhouses incorporating double transluscent walls, north side insulation and Collector Storage Tubes. A summary of this analysis for various versions of a commercially available greenhouse in incorporated as Table 1. An explanation of the analysis method is included in Appendix 1 as a case study.

From the economic analysis, it was concluded that the addition of Solar Collector Storage Tubes resulted in energy savings with a payback of approximately 5 years. The incorporation of added north side insulation in conjunction with the Solar Collector Storage Tubes on the free standing greenhouses resulted in paybacks of 2 1/2 years when compared with conventional electric heating. These results were encouraging enough to pursuade Kalwall to underwrite the cost of a small greenhouse testing program. The preliminary results of that testing program are described below.

The Experiment

In order to test the various effects of double glazing, north side insulation and added thermal mass in the form of Sun-Lite Solar Collector Storage Tubes, three small do-it-yourself greenhouses were constructed out of readily available building components. A sketch of the basic design is included as Figure 3. The greenhouse has a 4 ft. X 5 ft. base of 1" polystyrene foam. The two ends are each made of 3/4" CDX plywood, 4 ft. X 8 ft. with a 2 ft. radius curve cut at the top. The other two sides and roof are formed with a 5 ft. by approximately 18 ft. sheet of Kalwall's Sun-Lite material. The second greenhouse was formed by modifying the basic greenhouse with the addition of four 5 ft. tall black painted Sun-Lite Collector Storage Tubes, each containing 300 lbs. of water at the rear of the greenhouse. The third greenhouse was constructed containing an inner layer of a Sun-Lite material (in this case, Sun-Lite Premium) separated by a 1 1/2" air space from the external layer of Sun-Lite Regular. White reflective styrofoam insulation, 1" thick, was installed on the north, east and west sides of this greenhouse. Finally, four Sun-Lite Collector Storage Tubes painted black were also installed in this greenhouse and filled with 300 lbs. of water each.

The three greenhouses were installed along the south wall of Kalwall's test building.

- # 1 – A single glazed unit with very little thermal mass
- # 2 – A single glazed unit with 1,200 lbs. of thermal mass
- # 3 – A double glazed, north-insulated unit with 1,200 lbs. of thermal mass

Construction of these test greenhouses was completed towards the end of March, 1976 and instrumentation was installed during April, 1976.

NICHOLSON SOLAR ENERGY CATALOGUE

FIGURE 3
TEST GREENHOUSE #3
(Mailbox Design)

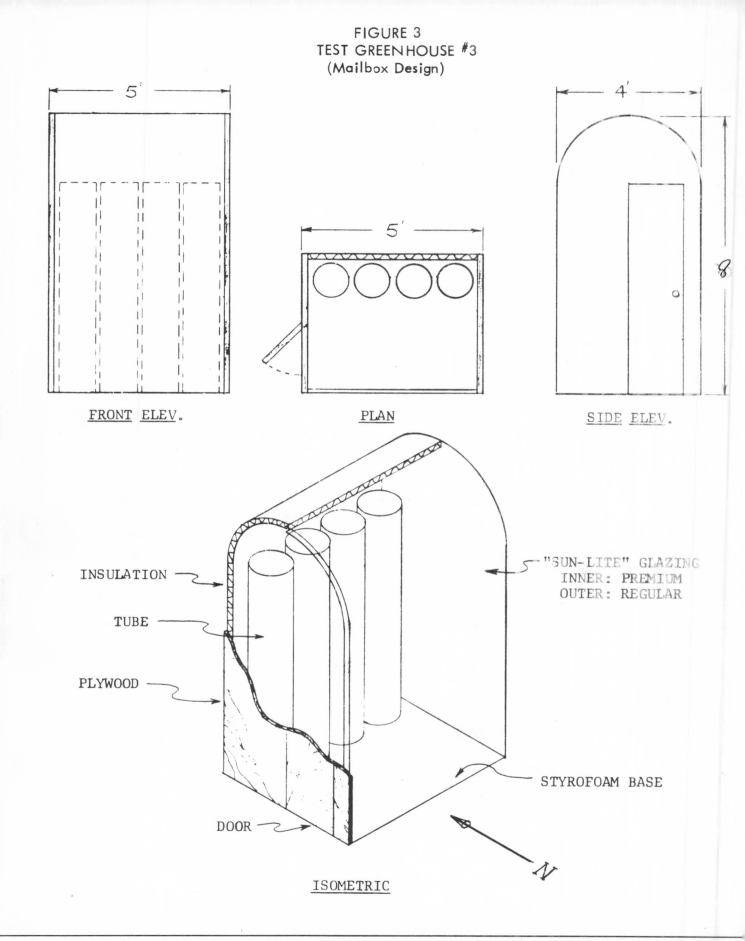

5'

FRONT ELEV.

5'

PLAN

4'

8'

SIDE ELEV.

INSULATION

TUBE

PLYWOOD

DOOR

"SUN-LITE" GLAZING
INNER: PREMIUM
OUTER: REGULAR

STYROFOAM BASE

N

ISOMETRIC

NICHOLSON SOLAR ENERGY CATALOGUE

The areas chosen for monitoring were the air temperatures at the top, bottom and rear sides of each greenhouse, the top and bottom tube temperatures at the centers of the tubes in selected tubes, outdoor ambient and the temperature of a device (Sunsor) used to measure the sun's intensity. The operation of a circulating fan added towards the end of the experiment was also monitored. This data was recorded on a Honeywell 24 point recorder which measured each data point every 48 seconds. A sample output from a typical day is included as Figure 4.

The Results

From the data traces recorded during the period from mid-March through mid-June, several facts became readily apparent. First, before the Collector Storage Tubes were added to the first greenhouse to be constructed, the double wall, north insulated model # 3 experienced maximum temperatures in the neighborhood of 100° F and minimum temperatures quite close to the ambient, despite its excellent thermal insulation. In fact, the thermal insulation was, in many cases, the cause of the undesirable 100° F temperatures. Of course, with proper venting, the daytime temperatures could have been limited and had the greenhouse been heated at night, it would have used much less energy than a single glazed version would have used. However, the purpose of the experiment was to investigate the stabilizing effect of thermal mass.

When thermal mass was added to this greenhouse, as expected, the temperatures were stabilized to the point where no temperatures went below 50° F. However, by this time spring was upon us and the daytime outdoor ambient during the day had risen high enough that the interior greenhouse temperatures were still approaching 100° F. Thus, it was confirmed that even during fairly cold days, a double cover greenhouse can produce temperatures which are injurious to plants unless it is vented. Secondly, it was found that even with thermal mass, well insulated greenhouses attain high undesirable temperatures in the springtime when the sun is high in the sky and local daytime ambients are quite warm. Therefore, either better coupled thermal mass or venting (which is undesirable in energy terms) is necessary.

With this in mind, the second greenhouse (# 2) was examined. This one was a single cover greenhouse with thermal mass. Further, the single cover greenhouse (# 1), without thermal mass was examined at the same time. In this fashion, we were able to isolate the effect of insulation versus the effect of the thermal mass. Essentially, the greenhouse with the single cover and thermal mass but no north insulation or double cover was able to collect and store virtually the same or more energy and maintain the same temperatures during the daytime. However, at night and during prolonged cold periods it lost its heat twice as fast, which was expected.

NICHOLSON SOLAR ENERGY CATALOGUE

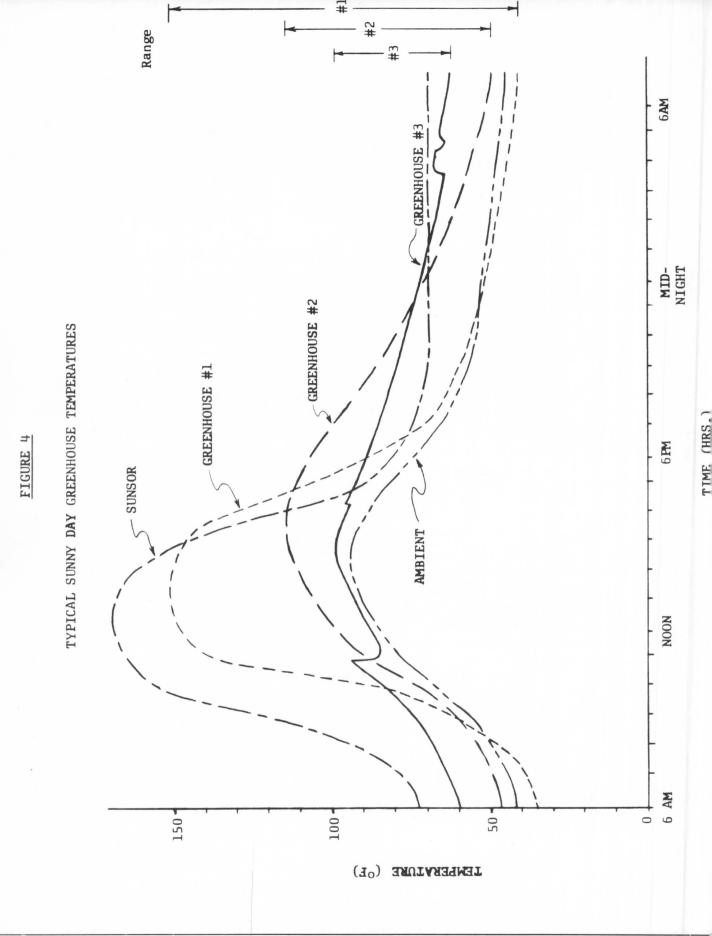

FIGURE 4

TYPICAL SUNNY DAY GREENHOUSE TEMPERATURES

In the weeks that followed, all the greenhouses began over-heating severly and an attempt was made to solve this problem without venting. A small circulating fan (18 watt, 60 cfm) was added at the top of greenhouse #3 to decrease air temperatures by circulating the hot air over the cooler tubes, thereby increasing the heat transfer coefficient. The fan was controlled by a thermostat installed at the top of the greenhouse set to turn on at 92° F. A second thermostat turned on the fan if the temperature at the front of the greenhouse went below 65° F. This thermostat thus caused the tubes to discharge more quickly when the outdoor ambient fell thus keeping the air throughout the greenhouse as warm as possible while eliminating cold spots.

The fan and thermostat performed as expected; they reduced the maximum air temperatures at the top of the greenhouse from about 110° F down to 95° F and they tended to even out the air temperature throughout the greenhouse while storing yet more heat in the tubes. Nevertheless, the weather was such that more than enough heat could be stored in the water in the tubes in the insulated greenhouse and over-heating occasionally occured, as shown in Tables II and III.

The performance of the greenhouse during a cold snap in May is summarized in these tables. Morning (M) and evening (E) temperatures were taken off the charts at 5:30 a.m. and at 5:30 p.m. respectively for each day. The top (T), front (F) and back (B) air temperatures within each greenhouse are listed as well as the water temperature of the top (T) and bottom (B) of two tubes in greenhouses #2 and #3. Also listed is the number of hours during each 12 hour period that the fan operated either because the top of #3 was too warm or the bottom too cold, thus keeping the temperature within acceptable limits.

Discussion Of Results

Perhaps the easiest way to understand the effect of both insulation and thermal mass on the performance of the greenhouses is to examine closely the following two parameters. First, the minimum temperature at the front of the greenhouse in the morning and second, the total temperature spread from morning to evening at the front of the greenhouse. These temperatures and others are listed in Tables II and III for each greenhouse.

Greenhouse #1, the single covered greenhouse, had wide variations of temperature. At night it closely followed the ambient and in some cases was even colder than the ambient temperature. This can be attributed to night sky radiation (on one cold day, this temperature was 35° F, 4° F below ambient). In the daytime, greenhouse #1 had a stagnation temperature which was in general 50-60° F above the ambient and had a maximum of 143° F. Often times this greenhouse had a variation in temperature from morning to evening of over 80° F. Clearly, single glazed greenhouses without thermal mass or ventilation are uninhabitable for plants.

TABLE II

	F 5/14		S 5/15		S 5/16		M 5/17		T 5/18		W 5/19		T 5/20	
	M	E	M	E	M	E	M	E	M	E	M	E	M	E
AMB	47	80	60	85	50	83	56	75	66	76	63	50	42	57
Greenhouse #1 T	45	125	60	130	50	130	57	90	66	93	62	52	42	91
Greenhouse #1 F	41	112	57	125	47	118	54	90	66	92	59	49	40	80
Greenhouse #1 B	43	108	57	116	48	105	54	89	65	89	60	50	40	73
Greenhouse #2 T	58	105	66	110	65	107	65	87	70	82	65	55	44	71
Greenhouse #2 F	52	97	63	106	59	103	61	81	67	80	63	52	42	71
Greenhouse #2 B	53	82	62	88	60	85	60	74	66	70	62	52	41	55
Tubes T	67	90	78	101	78	98	79	78	73	74	67	61	53	55
Tubes B	62	78	73	88	72	87	75	73	70	70	63	58	49	51
Tubes T	69	96	82	105	83	103	83	82	76	77	69	65	56	58
Tubes B	66	82	76	91	77	90	77	76	72	73	66	61	53	54
Greenhouse #3 T	74	97	78	106	81	105	82	92	78	92	71	70	59	80
Greenhouse #3 F	76	102	78	110	71	110	73	90	71	88	70	62	55	73
Greenhouse #3 B	73	94	72	103	79	102	81	88	77	84	65	67	58	68
Tubes T	85	98	88	107	91	107	94	92	86	86	77	75	66	67
Tubes B	77	86	80	94	82	95	85	83	79	78	71	67	60	60
Tubes T	79	92	84	101	88	100	90	87	82	82	75	71	62	63
Tubes B	74	85	79	93	81	93	84	82	77	77	70	66	60	59
Hours #3T>90°F.	10		0	12	1	12	2	3 1/2	0	1	0	0	0	0
Hours #3T<60°F.	0		0	0	0	0	0	0	0	0	0	9 1/2	12	10 1/2
Hours Sunsor	7 1/2		0	7	0	6 1/2	0	1	0	2	0	0	0	3

GREENHOUSE TEMPERATURES IN MAY OF 1976

NICHOLSON SOLAR ENERGY CATALOGUE

TABLE III

GREENHOUSE TEMPERATURES IN MAY OF 1976

	F 5/21 M	F 5/21 E	S 5/22 M	S 5/22 E	S 5/23 M	S 5/23 E	M 5/24 M	M 5/24 E	T 5/25 M	T 5/25 E	W 5/26 M	W 5/26 E	T 5/27 M	T 5/27 E	F 5/28 M	F 5/28 E
AMB	39	68	43	67	41	73	48	73	44	68	48	60	48	80	55	93
Greenhouse #1 T	40	100	42	108	40	125	47	125	44	119	49	75	49	130	55	143
Greenhouse #1 F	35	91	38	93	36	105	43	105	40	98	45	73	45	115	53	130
Greenhouse #1 B	37	93	40	101	38	103	45	103	42	94	47	71	47	106	55	123
Greenhouse #2 T	43	88	45	96	48	102	55	105	53	94	54	72	53	105	60	118
Greenhouse #2 F	40	66	44	84	45	91	52	88	49	87	52	66	50	90	60	105
Greenhouse #2 B	41	58	43	65	45	70	52	74	49	70	52	60	50	75	60	85
Tubes T	52	60	53	70	61	78	68	75	63	71	61	66	60	72	65	97
Tubes B	48	53	50	61	54	68	61	68	59	66	58	60	56	63	61	83
Tubes T	55	63	57	74	63	83	71	80	67	76	65	69	63	79	71	100
Tubes B	51	56	53	64	57	70	65	72	63	69	61	65	60	69	66	85
Greenhouse #3 T	56	92	57	92	60	92	68	92	66	92	65	80	64	92	70	100
Greenhouse #3 F	52	74	54	82	55	89	62	92	60	88	61	73	60	92	65	103
Greenhouse #3 B	55	72	58	77	60	83	68	85	60	80	65	72	62	85	70	97
Tubes T	61	68	63	77	68	84	74	83	73	81	71	76	69	79	75	99
Tubes B	56	60	56	65	61	71	67	73	66	72	65	67	60	70	69	86
Tubes T	57	64	50	70	62	77	70	78	68	75	67	71	65	76	74	93
Tubes B	54	58	55	63	57	70	67	71	65	70	64	67	61	70	69	84
Hours #3T>90°F.	0	1/2	0	1 1/2	0	5	0	2 1/2	0	1	0	0	0	8	0	8 1/2
Hours #3T<60°F.	12	7 1/2	12	4	10	4	5 1/2	2 1/2	7	5 1/2	5 1/2	6	5 1/2	3	0	0
Hours Sunsor	4 1/2	0	0	7	0	6	0	5	0	4	0	2	0	7	0	8

Greenhouse # 2, under the same weather conditions, experienced air temperatures which were not as closely related to the ambient. The temperatures of this greenhouse in the morning averaged some 10° – 15° F warmer than the ambient and the temperature spread from morning to evening was on the order of 35° – 45° F over typical sunny days. On sunny days, the maximum temperature often rose above 110° F. On the coldest day, the inside temperature fell to about 42° F, within 5° F of the outdoor ambient. It is clear from this information that although thermal mass helps moderate the environment inside a single glazed, unvented greenhouse, the thermal mass by itself is not enough.

Greenhouse # 3, which incorporated thermal mass, double glazing, north side insulation and circulating fan had much higher minimum temperatures than either greenhouse # 1 or # 2. In fact, during the entire two week period monitored, its minimum temperature never fell below the 55° F considered acceptable for most plants nightime temperature. Secondly, the average temperature spread for this greenhouse was on the order of 20° – 30° F, which is also acceptable. The only time in which the thermal environment in greenhouse # 3 was unacceptable to most plants was during a very sunny day following a previously sunny day. The fan and thermal mass system was unable to keep the temperatures below 92° F and in fact rose to 100° F or so. Under these conditions, it is felt that some venting must be incorporated to maintain reasonable temperatures in the greenhouse. It should be pointed out that during the entire 2 week period selected, none of the greenhouses were vented and none were provided with auxiliary heat. Only greenhouse # 3 containing all four modifications; thermal mass, insulation, double cover and constant air circulation did not require auxiliary heat to maintain reasonable temperatures.

Future Research

It is hoped that based on these results, further experiments will be conducted this summer to determine the usefulness of thermal mass in conjunction with nightime venting and constant air circulation to prevent over-heating. Testing of the final configuration will be carried out through the next winter to determine what percentage of the heat required by the greenhouse is provided by solar energy during the entire heating season.

Summary

After a review of the literature and preliminary economic analysis showed the technical and economic feasibility of incorporating thermal mass in the form of Kalwall's Solar Battery Collector Storage Tubes into greenhouses to increase the percentage of solar heat and save fuel, three greenhouses were constructed and tested successfully, demonstrating the concept. Additional improvements can be made through the use of constant air circulation and some venting to control daytime over-heating.

NICHOLSON SOLAR ENERGY CATALOGUE

Conclusion

1. Solar powered greenhouses are technically and economically feasible (and perhaps necessary) today.

2. Thermal mass, in the form of Kalwall's Solar Battery Collector Storage Tubes, can be cost effectively added to greenhouses to moderate or stabilize greenhouse temperatures variations without venting.

3. Constant air circulation greatly improves the temperature distribution, extremes and solar utilization of a greenhouse.

SECTION 8

NICHOLSON SOLAR ENERGY CATALOGUE

TABLE IV

GREENHOUSE PARAMETERS

Parameters	Units	#1	#2	#3	
Floor Area	sq. ft.	20	20	20	
Height	ft.	8	8	8	
Total Surface Area	sq. ft.	146	146	146	
South wall Area	sq. ft.	40	40	40	
Volume	cu. ft.	140	140	140	
Heat Capacity Greenhouse	BTU/$^{\circ}$F.	25	25	15	
Solar Transmittance	%	85-90	85-90	77%	
Number of Tubes	–	–	4-6' highx12" Dia.	4	
Weight	lbs.		1200	1200	
Heat Capacity-Water	BTU/$^{\circ}$F.	–	1200	1200	
Overall Heat Loss coefficient	BTU/$^{\circ}$F-HR				
Air to Ambient (UA$_1$)		118	118	42 Fan On	37 Fan Off
Tubes to Air (UA$_2$)			75	150	75
Heat Stored on Avg. Sunny Day (typically) BTU		Near 0	22800	19200	
Mass/sq. ft. face area	lbs. per sq. ft.	Near 0	30	30	

NICHOLSON SOLAR ENERGY CATALOGUE

APPENDIX I

Case Study

Solar Heat Model 5512

1. **BASIC HEATING REQUIREMENT:**
   Surface Area x (U x 24) + infiltration = Q
   196 square feet x (13.2) + 168 = 2750 BTU/DD
   Solar Supplies 20% therefore,
   2750 x .8 x 6000 DD = <u>132 THERMS</u>/all electric required/year

2. **MODIFICATIONS, COST:**

Add 10 tubes (10" x 8' black)	@ $30.00	$ 300.00
Cost of space $.75/ft. or 7 '0' panels	@ $15.50	108.50
Wood, labor, water, etc.		91.50
	TOTAL	$ 500.00

3. **NEW HEATING REQUIREMENTS:**
   238 x 13.2 + 228 = 3370 BTU/DD
   3370 x .8 x 6000 DD = <u>161 THERMS</u>   Electric required if no water in tubes

4. **SOLAR HEAT PROVIDED:**
   <u>Tubes</u>   1098 BTU/sq. ft. — Sunny Day Tilted Gain Solar Battery
            x 50% cloudy
            <u>550 BTU</u>/AVG Day Contribution
   80 square feet x .8 x 550 BTU/DAY x 270 Days/Season = <u>95 THERMS</u> by Tubes

5. **NEW ELECTRIC REQUIREMENT:**
   161 – 95 = <u>66 THERMS</u> Electric required
   Saving = $\overline{132 - 66}$ = 66 THERMS
               = 1933 KWH
               = $ 96.68/Season @ $.05/KWH = $1.46/THERM

6. **PAY BACK PERIOD:**
   $\frac{500}{96.68}$ = <u>5 YEARS</u>

REFERENCES

1. Acme, The Greenhouse Climate Control Handbook, Acme Engineering and Manufacturing Corporation, Muskogee, Oklahoma, Form C7G 10/75.

2. Bruce Anderson, Solar Energy Home Design in Four Climates, May 1975, Church Hill, Harrisville, New Hampshire 03450.

3. ASHRAE, 1972 Handbook of Fundamentals, 345 East 47th Street, New York, New York 10017.

4. John Zusianovich-Zomeworks, Solar heated greenhouse with a one-year payout, 1300 Arizona N.W., Alburquerque, New Mexico 87110.

5. T.A. Lawand, Solar Energy Journal, Brace Research Institute, MacDonald College of McGill University, Ste. Anne de Bellerrue, Quebec, Canada H9X 3M1, SRENA 17(5) 269-324 (1975).

6. R.F. Lucas, Application of Solar Heated Water to Greenhouses, University of Florida, Gainsville, Florida, AREC, Bradenton Research Report, GC-1976-3.

7. Robert T. Nash, Temperature Stabilization in Greenhouses, July 28, August 1, 1975, Vandervilt University, Nashville, Tennessee.

8. New Alchemists, Dr. John Todd, Woods Hole, Massachusetts.

9. Vegetable Factory, Product Literature, 100 Court Street, Copiague, New York 11726, 1975, Vegetable Factory, Inc.

SECTION 9

ADVANCED INSULATION TECHNIQUES

INSULATION AND AIR TIGHTNESS

This dissertation is based in part on conversations with John Hodkinson and the practical experience gained from applying these concepts in the field.

Heat wants to travel omnidirectionally from hot to cold. Insulation provides a resistance to that heat flow. There is no way that you can stop heat energy from flowing. The best that you can do is slow it down.

While it is true that heat wants to flow towards relatively colder areas in any direction, it is equally true that it will flow relatively faster if that direction is upward. This is why we use higher insulation values in roofs and ceilings and progressively lesser values in walls and still less in floors.

The effectiveness of insulation is indicated by its "R" or "U" value. R = 1/U. The higher the "R" or the lower the "U", the better the insulation material.

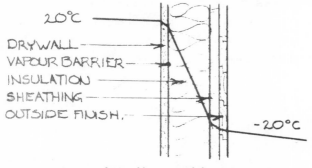

Typical Wall Assembly

Insulation resists the flow of heat. Most of the drop in temperature from inside to outside happens in the insulation.

Note the vapor barrier to keep the house moisture from condensing in the insulation.

Selecting the Right Insulation Material

There are many types of insulating materials available. Selecting the proper one for a specific application depends on several factors. Some of these factors include the following:

1. Budget: Some of the insulating materials have a high purchase cost and a low installation cost while others have a low purchase cost and a high installation cost. The average budget usually has a short supply of either money or labor. When money is in short supply and labor is plentiful, the choice would be towards low cost insulation materials. The converse, plentiful money and scarce labor, would occasion the choice of a high cost insulation material that requires minimum labor.(ie. sprayed on polyurethane is the most expensive insulation material available but uses a bare minimum of labor in application. The entire roof and all the walls of Solar V were insulated in less than a day.)

NICHOLSON SOLAR ENERGY CATALOGUE

2. Experience: Some of the techniques outlined require a fairly high degree of proficiency for successful application. Match your choice of the insulating technique to the skils available.

3. Maintenance: Insulation properly installed should not require maintenance. Some examples of insulation techniques gone wrong include destruction of the insulation by rodent penetration due to the lack of mouse barriers and excessive matting of fiberglass insulation due to poor venting and/or lack of proper vapor barriers. A recent fad of spraying polyurethane over a structure and then simply painting the surface (to shield out harmful ultra-violet rays and improve the appearance) has shown a tendency towards deterioration due to exposure and mechanical damage.

There is a process available which is sold under the name of "Dryvit" (manufactured by BASF Industries) that offsets this problem of maintenance. Basically, it is a process that allows you to bond a cementatious base product (with good weathering characteristics) over a petroleum based product (such as styrene, urethane, etc.) where normally these materials are incompatible and resist bonding. The process involves the adhesion of a fiberglas cloth to the insulating material by employing the use of a primus. This in turn is covered with a finish coating giving a stucco effect of lasting durability.

An example of Dryvit applied to a Nicholson home. The house has been in service for four years and the Dryvit surface shows no signs of deterioration.

The relative merits of various insulation techniques are outlined in the following chart.

9—2

RELATIVE MERITS OF INSULATION TECHNIQUES USED IN NICHOLSON HOMES

Insulating Material	Relative Purchase Cost	Relative Installation Cost	[1]Insulation Value	[2]Cost per Foot Board Measure	Durability	Comments
Fiberglas Bats	Low	High	R = 3.5	4¢	Good	Extremely susceptible to poor installation techniques. Cannot be used below ground. Non flammable.
Foamboard	Low to Medium	Medium	R = 4.0	10¢	Poor	Foamboard is composed of styrene beads. Moisture has a tendency to infiltrate between these beads causing deterioration. Also tends to shrink with time. Crumbles easily when handled. Flammable.[3]
Styrene	Medium	Medium	R = 5.0	20¢	Excellent	Cannot be exposed to sunlight for long periods of time. Flammable.
Polyurethane foamed in place	Very High	Very Low	R = 7.5 to 9.0	40¢	Excellent	Excellent for air tightness. Do not expose to sunlight for long lengths of time. Flammable.
Aluminum Foil Air Sandwich	Very Low	High	4 layers, 3 air spaces, R = 20	.5¢	Varies	Experience in northern climates shows that rodent penetration is almost impossible to prevent. Subsequent damage drastically reduces the insulation value.

1. Values may vary according to source of supply.
2. Prices may vary in different locals. A foot board measure is 1" x 12" x 12". This is one reason that I use them outside a fire break such as gypsum board.
3. Petroleum based products are flammable.

NICHOLSON SOLAR ENERGY CATALOGUE

Air Tightness and Vapor Barriers

The bear wears his fur on the outside of his skin... A good key governing the use of insulation.

The basic rule to adhere to when designing insulation systems is to provide continuous vapor and air tightness on the warm side of the insulated surface. This bears repetition. The vapor and air tightness is needed on the side of the insulated surface that is closest to the interior living space.

Note: There is a school of thought based upon the principle that if one is good, two is better. This school of thought advocates vapor barriers on both sides of the insulated surface. This is incorrect. The object is to prevent all the moisture generated during the course of daily living (ie. running baths, washing dishes, etc.) from migrating through the inside wall and contaminating the insulation. If any moisture finds its way into the insulating layer, it is imperative that it be vented off. A vapor barrier on the outside traps the moisture in the insulating layer where it reduces the effectiveness of the insulation and rots any wood that it comes in contact with.

Another effect of poor vapor and air barriers is the discomfort caused by drafts, uneven heating and dryness of living spaces.

Polyethylene film is a differentially permeable membrane that is commonly used as a vapor barrier. Its function is to inhibit the flow of moisture while permitting the flow of air. The air flow through polyethylene is not considerable and for all practical purposes can serve as an air tight layer when applied continuously with no tears or seams left unsealed. However, given the choice of vapor barriers, I would choose aluminum foil which is both vapor and air tight and includes the bonus of a reflective surface which re-radiates some of the short wave heat radiation back into the room.

NICHOLSON SOLAR ENERGY CATALOGUE

Another common form of vapor barrier is paper backed fiberglas insulation. This form of insulation is usually stapled between the studs and rafters. Unless extreme care is taken, this method of application produces many air and vapor leaks along the sides of the studs and rafters to which it is attached and at the point where the individual sheets meet.

Venting

Moisture damage attributed to condensation has caused an emphasis to be placed on increasing ventilation to the insulation. This practice will help alleviate the condensation problem. The danger in so doing however, is that you may increase infiltration losses at the same time. Some venting is necessary but excessive venting should be avoided.

One way to accomplish this is to keep moisture in the house where it belongs. The excessive use of humidifiers is a strong indication that the house insulation has poor vapor protection. Thusfar, none of the houses built using the continuous vapor and air tight layer have required the services of a humidifier. It seems that we have struck a balance between the humidity lost from fireplaces, windows, etc. and the humidity gained from the normal processes of daily living.

This picture shows tape covering the junction of the foil backed gypsum board wall covering and the styrene foundation insulation. Not showing in the picture is the non-hardening butyl sealant applied to the joint between these surfaces prior to taping.

NICHOLSON SOLAR ENERGY CATALOGUE

Installing expanded mesh wire as a mouse shield. Expanded mesh has an advantage over conventional solid flashing because it serves the function of a mouse shield and still permits air passage to the insulation vents.

Application of the inexpensive and efficient non-hardening butyl sealant over electric boxes and access holes for electric wiring.

Fiberglas insulation behind and in front of electrical wires

Insulation in place and covered with exterior grade plywood

NICHOLSON SOLAR ENERGY CATALOGUE

To Sum Up

Heat flows to cold. Insulation slows it up.

There are many insulating techniques to choose from. A correct choice is the result of thorough planning.

Keep it air tight. When you need fresh air, open a window. That is what they were designed for.

Humidity will serve you better inside the house rather than inside the walls.

A well insulated house is not necessarily an expensive house. Sealant is inexpensive and when applied properly, can save lots of money (which is fun to have).

When in doubt, ask (and study).

Learn from nature. All the secrets are there, ready to reveal themselves to the inquiring mind.

Conventional construction grade lumber is usually "mill pond dry". In other words, soaking wet. As it dries out, it shrinks and warps, producing a prime source of air leaks.

Strive to keep your air tight layer continuous.

Unless you are an extreme form of nature lover, keep the mice out. Squirrels too. We used to have a squirrel feeder until I noticed that they were moving into the house to be near to their food supply.

Caulk, caulk, caulk . . . Tape, tape, tape . . .

SECTION 10

EDUCATIONAL MATERIAL

— NOTES —

NICHOLSON SOLAR ENERGY CATALOGUE

The following pages review some of the many excellent books on energy.

If any of them are unavailable from your local bookseller, contact the Nicholson Solar Energy Catalogue at Box 344, Ayer's Cliff, Quebec, Canada, J0B 1C0 and we will see that your request is fulfilled.

Solar Heated Buildings, A Brief Survey

by W.A. Shurcliff (300 pages)

Highly recommended. Provides an excellent base for anyone attempting to design a solar installation. Contains sketches and specifications for 319 solar heated homes, schools and commercial buildings with 79 photographs by Peter Hollander.

SOLAR HEATED BUILDINGS A BRIEF SURVEY

Jan. 15, 1977

13th
and *final*
edition

W. A. Shurcliff

19 Appleton St., Cambridge, MA. 02138

**With special supplement:
79 photographs by Peter Hollander**

Copyrighted

SCOPE OF SURVEY

We include houses, schools, commercial buildings that are partially or fully solar heated. We include buildings that did exist, do exist, or are expected to exist very soon. Total number included: 319.

Buildings in USA are discussed by states, alphabetically (Alabama, Ariz., California, etc.). Then buildings in foreign countries are discussed.

We are greatly indebted to many owners, inventors, architects, and solar engineers for supplying important information not generally available.

Price in USA:	$12 if check enclosed with order. $13 otherwise. Add $2 if shipment by first class mail is desired.
Outside USA:	$12 if check enclosed with order. $14 otherwise. Add $4 if shipment by air is desired.
Make out check to:	Wm A Shurcliff and mail to 19 Appleton St., Cambridge, MA 02138

NICHOLSON SOLAR ENERGY CATALOGUE

SECTION 10

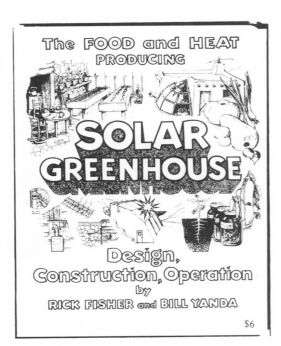

The Food and Heat Producing Solar Greenhouse

by Rick Fisher and Bill Yanda

Loaded with practical information on the design, construction and operation of solar greenhouses. We intend to incorporate some of the ideas into our greenhouse project here at Ayer's Cliff.

The Solar Home Book

by Bruce Anderson

A well illustrated and clearly written book. Includes all the fundamentals on solar energy.

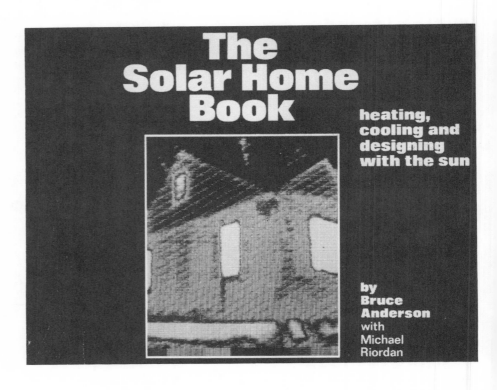

NICHOLSON SOLAR ENERGY CATALOGUE

keeping the heat in
HOW TO RE-INSULATE YOUR HOME
TO SAVE ENERGY AND MONEY
(AND BE MORE COMFORTABLE TOO)

Energy, Mines and   Energie, Mines et
Resources Canada   Ressources Canada

Keeping The Heat In

by Energy, Mines and Resources Canada

Excellent guide for retrofitting older buildings. Available in english or french by writing to: Keeping The Heat In, P.O. Box 900, Westmount Postal Station, Montreal, Quebec H3Z 2V1. No cost.

Description of Some Solar Heated Houses in Canada

by Brace Research Institute

Excellent report providing current solar radiation charts for all of Canada. Pictures, diagrams and specifications for 10 Canadian solar homes. This technical report number T. 103 is available for $2.50 directly from Brace Research Institute, Macdonald College of McGill University, Ste. Anne de Bellevue, Quebec H0A 1C0.

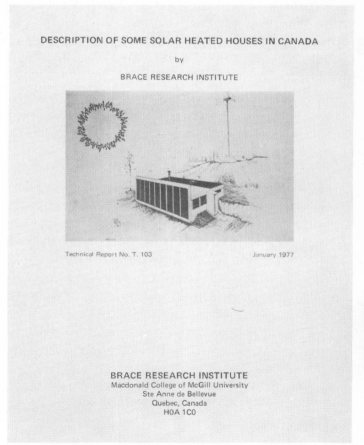

DESCRIPTION OF SOME SOLAR HEATED HOUSES IN CANADA

by

BRACE RESEARCH INSTITUTE

Technical Report No. T. 103   January 1977

BRACE RESEARCH INSTITUTE
Macdonald College of McGill University
Ste Anne de Bellevue
Quebec, Canada
H0A 1C0

NICHOLSON SOLAR ENERGY CATALOGUE

Environmentally Appropriate
Technology

by Bruce McCallum

Up to date information on the latest
achievements involving high technology. Not lacking in practical
information. Sections on biomass,
heat pumps, wind, hydro and so on. . .

Additional Copies

Additional copies of the Nicholson Solar Energy Catalogue can be obtained by
sending $ 9.50 plus 50¢ postage to:

Nicholson Solar Energy Catalogue
P.O. Box 125
Ayer's Cliff, Quebec
Canada   J0B 1C0

Update Service Included.
Quantity discounts available.

Nick Nicholson conducting a seminar at Bishops University

This model of an air / rock solar system is available for purchase or rental.   Contact the Catalogue for further information.

Nick Nicholson is available for speaking engagements, workshops and seminars. For information write to: Nicholson Solar Energy Catalogue, P.O. Box 344, Ayer's Cliff, Quebec, Canada J0B 1C0.

SECTION 10

NICHOLSON SOLAR ENERGY CATALOGUE

The Solar Frontier

- Solar heated houses in the snowbelt
- Houses for the average income family
- Their cost, performance and technology
- Told by the architects and by the people who live in them.

A 25 minute colour film about solar heated homes in the snowbelt:

Their costs, technology and feasibility.

The film is available for either purchase or rental from:

The Canadian Filmmakers Distribution Center
406 Jarvis Street
Toronto, Ontario
(416) 921 – 4121

Rental Cost: $30   Purchase Cost: $390

Directed and Produced by
Frances and Peter Mellen

A Mellenco Film Production
16 m.m., 25 min.,
colour, sound.

NICHOLSON SOLAR ENERGY CATALOGUE

SECTION 11

PRICE LIST
FOR SOLAR COMPONENTS

NICHOLSON SOLAR ENERGY CATALOGUE

GUIDELINE

Bill of materials for the solar system for Solar VI.

Item	Quantity	Cost in Canada*
Aluminum Collector	448 sq. ft.	$ 165.76
Epoxy paint and primer	2 gallons	36.00
Firring strips	648 lineal ft.	38.88
Cedar glazing bars	536 lineal ft.	64.32
.040 Sun-lite Premium glazing	448 sq. ft.	403.20
Crushed stone	30 tons	180.00
Styrene insulation	1296 footboard measure	285.12
Aspenite to cover rock store	6 sheets	36.00
R-32 fiberglas insulation	168 sq. ft.	84.00
Concrete blocks (plenums)	52	26.00
Spruce 2" x 4" x 12'	8	8.00
Ductwork	As outlined	150.00
Dayton blower	1	130.00
Hawthome differential controller	1	90.00
Power dampers	2	280.00
Back flow damper	1	20.00
Nortron electric furnace	1	325.00
White Rodger store sensor	1	34.00
Misc. tape, nails, sealant	-	60.00
TOTAL		$ 2,416.28

For estimating purposes, add approximately 100 man hours labor and deduct the cost of installing a conventional heating system.

* At this time, we are paying 17.5% Federal Customs Duty, 12% Federal Tax and 8% Provincial Tax where applicable on all components. These levies are included in the prices quoted.

NICHOLSON SOLAR ENERGY CATALOGUE

CURRENT PRICES

Information on prices and availability for any of the materials shown or mentioned in this manual may be obtained by contacting:

In Canada

Solerco Ltd.
Solar Energy Division
P.O. Box 211, Under Bunker Road
Ayer's Cliff, Quebec J0B 1C0
(819) 838 - 5935

In the United States

Kalwall Corporation
Solar Components Division
P.O. Box 237
Manchester, New Hampshire 03105
(603) 668 - 8186

Or, by sending a self addressed, stamped envelope to:

The Nicholson Solar Energy Catalogue
P.O. Box 125
Ayer's Cliff, Quebec
Canada J0B 1C0

Please note the information on page 12-7 if writing to the catalogue.

Please note that an expanded list of responsible suppliers will be included in future editions of the catalogue.

NICHOLSON SOLAR ENERGY CATALOGUE

SECTION 12

MISCELLANEOUS

HOUSE OF COMMONS
CANADA

CHARLES L. CACCIA
M.P. FOR DAVENPORT

TELEPHONE
OTTAWA (613) 992-2576
TORONTO (416) 654-8048

BILL   C-309

An Act Respecting The Domestic
And Industrial Use Of Solar Energy

Remarks by Charles Caccia, M.P. for Davenport,

to   the

Standing Committee On National Resources And Public Works

March 30, 1977

NICHOLSON SOLAR ENERGY CATALOGUE

Mr. Chairman, members of the Committee:

It is indeed an honour to introduce to you today bill C-309, "an Act respecting the domestic and industrial use of solar energy". By "solar energy", I mean all renewable resources - not only solar energy used for space heating and cooling, but energy derived from wind, biomass, tidal and geothermal sources. The bill refers to all renewable resources, although for the purpose of this discussion, the emphasis is on solar space heating.

Before we get into the specifics of bill C-309, I would like to explain briefly why this bill was introduced. The growing cost and depletion of non-renewable resources makes it essential for Canada to develop alternative sources of energy. Renewable resources have two advantages in the sense that they are unlimited and compatible with the environment. By introducing this bill last June, I hoped to draw attention to the solar option and urge more intensive efforts to develop and demonstrate viable solar technology.

The other important reason is to promote and stimulate the creation of a Canadian industry producing solar equipment and parts. In this country, we have unique features of climate and geography which necessitate a distinctly Canadian technology if solar heating is to become a useful energy resource. By producing solar equipment suitable for Canadian conditions in Canada, we would ensure Canadian control over this technology and avoid having to rely on imported research or solar equipment. We would also stimulate innovation in Canadian industry and create thousands of jobs stemming from the production of solar technology. According to Dr. Phil Cockshutt, Co-ordinator of the National Research Centre Energy Project, for example, solar heating could eventually become a billion-dollar-a-year industry in Canada.* We will benefit from the solar option, not only because we will have alternative sources of energy, but because we will be able to reap the economic and industrial benefits of the production and application of solar equipment as well.

It was primarily with these two thoughts in mind that I took the initiative of introducing bill C-309. The general goal of the bill is to promote the use of solar energy in Canada. Specifically, it calls for the creation of an "Institute of Solar Energy Application" which, once established, will encourage and assist solar developments.

As I see it, the Institute would:

> Assist and encourage the development, demonstration and production of solar energy technology for domestic and industrial use.

> Stimulate the establishment of a Canadian industry producing solar energy equipment and parts with the help of programs like the new Enterprise Development Program sponsored by the Department of Industry, Trade and Commerce.

---

* Quoted from Dr. Phil Cockshutt, Solar Energy, SCITEC Briefing, Energy Project, National Research Council (February, 1977).

NICHOLSON SOLAR ENERGY CATALOGUE

Inform the public about the uses of solar energy and encourage public participation in energy conservation and solar energy utilization.

Assist in removing institutional barriers to solar energy and urge provincial and municipal governments to take steps to encourage the use of solar energy through through tax incentives, special hydro rates, etc.

Help developing nations interested in developing their own svolar technology and reduce their costly dependence on oil imports.

The Institute would function much like other institutes in Canada, such as the C.D. Howe Research Institute in Montreal or the Canadian Institute for International Affairs in Toronto. In addition to the above mentioned goals, the proposed Institute would make policy recommendations to the government, assist in co-ordinating government programs in the field of renewable energy, and help Canadians understand what is being done in the public sector. The establishment of the Institute would also help to generate confidence for homeowners who today are waiting for guarantees before they invest capital in solar research and development or install solar heating in their homes. Performing these functions, the Institute would make a significant contribution towards the utilization of renewable sources of energy in Canand.

By approving this bill, this Committee and the House of Commons would:

Recognize, through Parliament, the importance of the solar option in Canada's energy future.

Give parliamentary endorsement to the importance of developing solar energy technology for domestic and industrial use.

Indicate support, in principle, for initiatives taken in the area of developing renewable resources.

Support the development of a solar technology based on Canadian requirements and promote the establishment of a new industry based on the production of solar technology.

Parliamentary approval of this bill would make an important contribution to the domestic use of solar energy and the establishment of solar industry in this country.

In Canada today, comprehensive efforts are required if the utilization of renewable resources is to take place on a wide scale. The establishment of a solar Institute would be but the first step. It is quite possible, if Canada makes a serious commitment to renewable energy sources, that the Institute would take on greater responsibilities. The Institute, for example, could become an agency which would assume responsibility for the renewable energy program as a whole - a program which at present is divided between four federal departments, the Ministries of Science and Technology (the National Research Council);

Energy, Mines and Resources; Fisheries and the Environment; and Agriculture Canada. Indeed, the government would do well to look into the merits of establishing a crown agency in charge of renewable resources as it did when Atomic Energy of Canada was established for nuclear energy. Another possibility would be to consider giving responsibility for renewable energy to an agency already in existence, such as Petro Canada. It stands to reason that an agency like Petro Canada, primarily concerned with the production and distribution of non-renewable resources would incorporate in its mandata the use and application of renewable energy. One would complement the other.

Any one of these developments or a number of others might take place once a solar Institute is established. But the creation of an Institute is the first step. It is an important one if we are to succeed in developing solar technology and promoting the application of renewable resources all across Canada.

At this point, it seems to me we have reached a cross-roads as far as deciding how far we will commit ourselves to the development of the solar option in this country. The importance of solar energy to Canada's energy future is understood. Public interest and concern for solar energy is increasing by leaps and bounds and, in fact, is far ahead of present technical and commercial realities. And, as I mentioned earlier, solar energy could mean thousands and the growth of a whole new industry in Canada.

But in this country so far, we have only begun to explore the potential of adopting the solar option. Other countries such as the United States, Australia and Japan are investing substantial sums in the development and demonstration of viable solar technology. If we wait too long, Canadian manufacturers may not be able to compete, even in the home market, with technology produced abroad. And in this country, we are still facing a multitude of technical, social and institutional barriers which make the decision to adopt solar home heating a difficult one for many potential buyers.

Look briefly at what is happening in the United States today. The U.S. budget for solar energy, which is managed under the auspices of the U.S. Energy Research and Development Administration (ERDA), is $290 million in the fiscal year 1976-77. $305 million is requested for the next fiscal year for renewable resources alone. A National Solar Heating and Cooling Information Centre has been established with a toll free number to provide information about solar energy. And the U.S. is moving to consolidate its energy program, now divided between several jurisdictions, into one department. In the U.S. solar energy is being given a high priority and the national government has played a leading role in conducting research and establishing demonstration programs.

In Canada, similar initiative has to be taken. The potential of solar heating as a renewable energy source, and the prospect of large-scale commercial activity in solar technology are substantial and warrant a strong commitment.

For example, a study carried out by K.G.T. Hollands and J.F. Orgill of the Waterloo Research Institute, entitled, "Potential for Solar Heating in Canada" and published in February, concludes the following:

NICHOLSON SOLAR ENERGY CATALOGUE

For 1976 and 1980 energy prices, short-term storage systems supplemented by oil or natural gas should be sized to provide about 50% of a building's total energy demands, if total costs are to be minimized.

Short-term storage systems so supplemented by oil can be cost-competitive in 1976 with 100% oil systems for some building types and some cities in Canada.

By 1980, short-term storage systems supplemented by oil will be cost-effective against 100% oil systems for heating well-insulated single family dwellings in every Canadian city simulated, provided the high-price oil scenario holds, the low-price solar hardware scenario holds, and money is available at 9% interest rates. If some or all of these conditions do not apply, combined solar-oil systems may not be cost-effective (that is, the two costs should be within about 30% of each other).

These conclusions point out that solar heating systems supplemented by oil or natural gas are already capable of contributing to Canada's energy requirements. But as yet we have a long way to go before the commercial adoption of solar heating makes this contribution a truly significant one.

The economic benefits to be gained by introducing solar technology on a wide scale are also substantial, but again, they will only be achieved if concerted efforts are made. In a SCITEC Brief entitled, "Solar Energy", presented in February, Dr. Cockshutt makes the following observations:

"If we look forward seventy-five or one hundred years, the oil and gas on which we presently rely for space heating will be exhausted.

"It is clear...that a determined technological effort now is essential to evolve economic, efficient and durable solar heating systems. Having in mind the slow diffusion of new technology in the construction industry, a major push is justified immediately, but the rate of implementation should not be overly accelerated...

"Whether solar energy supplies 30% or 90% of the space heating requirements in 2050 A.D., it will represent an enormous commercial activity and opportunity."

The potential benefits of solar energy, therefore, are substantial. The Minister of Energy, Mines and Resources recently stated, "Renewable energy clearly is one of man's great hopes for the future." I agree with him and hope the members of this Committee will join in approving this bill.

NICHOLSON SOLAR ENERGY CATALOGUE

— NOTES —

WHEN WRITING TO THE CATALOGUE

Everybody loves to receive mail and we at the catalogue office are no exception.
We love hearing all of your comments, criticisms and questions. But we are also
very busy building, designing and publishing so, if you write us and wish a response
it will help us greatly if you follow the following suggestions:

1.   Always include a stamped, self addressed envelope.

2.   If you have any questions that require a response, leave plenty of room in your
        letter between each question.

This way, we can write the answer down immediately upon reading the letter, place
it in the envelope that you supply and mail it out that same day.